STAR WARS

TIE FIGHTER

Owners' Workshop Manual

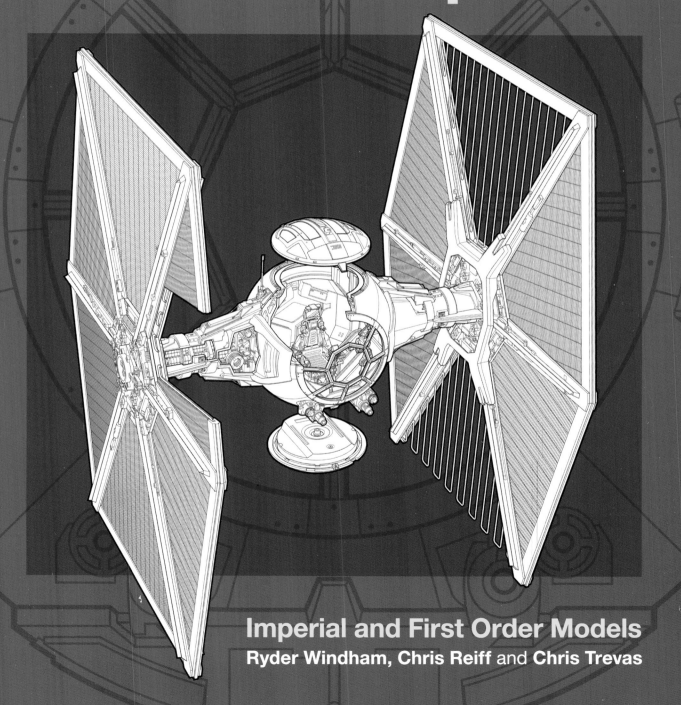

Imperial and First Order Models

Ryder Windham, Chris Reiff and **Chris Trevas**

CONTENTS

TIE FIGHTER

SIENAR FLEET SYSTEMS AND THE TIE SERIES

The leading manufacturer of military starfighters and shuttles in the galaxy, Sienar Fleet Systems originated as Republic Sienar Systems, a corporation that specialized in the design and production of customized spacecraft for affluent clients in the Galactic Republic. Engineer and designer Raith Sienar headed his corporation with minimal self-promotion, and was, according to numerous reports, less interested in recognition than technical challenges and customer satisfaction. Sienar devoted himself to designing advanced starships while maintaining professional discretion for his more secretive clientele.

During the Clone Wars, Sienar Fleet Systems remained dedicated to the Republic, and manufactured military shuttles and landing craft for the Republic Navy. The Navy also commissioned Sienar to manufacture a prototype corvette, a stealth ship equipped with an experimental cloaking device—reportedly developed by Republic engineers—that rendered the ship invisible and undetectable to standard scanners and sensors. Republic forces used the spear-shaped stealth ship to destroy a Separatist dreadnought, but the cloaking technology's enormous expense and maintenance requirements discouraged the Navy from commissioning additional stealth ships.

After the end of the Clone Wars, and the Republic gave way to the Galactic Empire, Imperial authorities immediately transitioned the Grand Army of the Republic and Republic Navy into the Imperial Army and Navy. Determined to quell any and all rebel opposition, the Empire's regional Governor of the Outer Rim, Grand Moff Wilhuff Tarkin, commissioned Sienar to create a line of single-pilot, short-range starfighters for the Navy. Tarkin mandated that the weaponized fighters should be extremely fast and maneuverable, energy efficient, and inexpensive to manufacture.

Raith Sienar personally designed the fighters. The result was a central spherical pod positioned between two hexagonal solar energy-collecting wings. The pod contained the fighter's cockpit, and was backed by a pair of ion engines. The acronym for "twin ion engines" gave the starfighter its name: TIE fighter.

To minimize power drain and maximize maneuverability, Sienar eschewed typically standard systems such as deflector shields and a hyperdrive. After a series of test flights, the Empire approved Sienar's design, and executed an exclusive contract with Sienar for the production of TIE fighters, and the development of other Imperial vessels.

Sienar produced a prototype Imperial Interdictor cruiser, which carried experimental gravity well projectors that could shut down hyperdrive units in nearby craft, and thus prevent enemy ships from fleeing into hyperspace. Unfortunately, while pursuing a rebel ship, the Interdictor accidentally captured its own escort craft, which resulted in a collision that destroyed the prototype. Imperial investigators determined that Sienar was not responsible for the accident.

Although Sienar executives had hoped that the Interdictor would lead to more opportunities to manufacture cruisers and other warships for the Empire, their contract to produce TIE fighters protected their economic interests, and also helped secure Sienar's place in galactic history.

ORIGINS AND DEVELOPMENT

During the twilight years of the Galactic Republic, Raith Sienar experimented with unorthodox spacecraft technologies in his Advanced Projects Laboratory. One development from this lab was an armed Star Courier, which Sienar conceived for wealthy diplomats and business executives who traveled in dangerous areas. The Star Courier had a central spherical cabin for crew and passengers, and an experimental high-temperature ion engine system that required large radiator panels, which folded inward during landings. The courier's defenses included laser cannons and exotic sensor systems.

Declassified records from Imperial Facility 729-D revealed the existence of the *Scimitar*, a customized Star Courier manufactured by Sienar Design Systems. The *Scimitar* was equipped with a "cloak field generator," also known as an invisibility field projector, a cloaking device that scientists had regarded as theoretical until the discovery of the rare stygium crystals on the volcanically

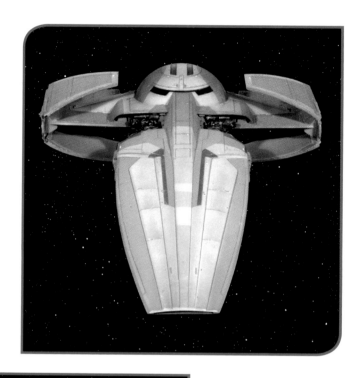

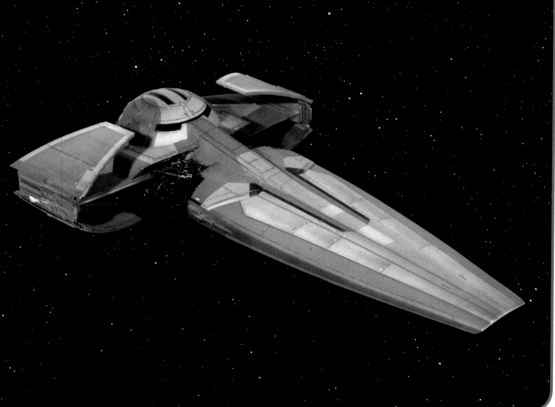

▲ A heavily customized Star Courier, Darth Maul's *Scimitar* had a spherical cabin and a wing configuration that foreshadowed the design of the Imperial TIE fighter.

◄ Sienar designed the *Scimitar*'s folding wings with radiator panels large enough to power the high-temperature ion engine, and an unconventional extended hood to house the cloak field generator.

turbulent planet Aeten II in the Outer Rim. Unlike a standard Star Courier, the *Scimitar* had a long, extended hood that housed the cloak field generator, additional weapons, and compartments for cargo.

Related records identified the customized courier as the property of the Sith Lord Darth Maul. Given historical accounts of Maul's affiliation with Sheev Palpatine, the eventual head of the Galactic Empire, Imperial historians hypothesize the probability that Sienar customized the courier for Palpatine, who sourced schematics for the cloaking device, and bestowed the courier to Maul. Historians also surmise that Palpatine was the principal source of similar schematics that Republic engineers provided to Sienar for the construction of a prototype corvette stealth ship during the Clone Wars.

After Grand Moff Tarkin commissioned Raith Sienar to design a prototype for an Imperial starfighter, Sienar drew from his own design of the Star Courier, and also from two single-pilot, short-range starfighters that Sienar's chief competitor, Kuat Systems Engineering, had manufactured for Republic Navy pilots during the Clone Wars: the Alpha-3

▲ Mass-produced for Republic forces during the Clone Wars, each V-wing starfighter carried a single clone trooper pilot who wore a pressure suit and helmet.

▼ Kuat Systems Engineering built the Eta-2 *Actis* Interceptor with a pressurized cockpit for a single Jedi pilot, who operated without bulky flight instruments or energy shield projectors, and relied instead on the Jedi's own allegedly mystical powers to pursue and destroy targets.

Nimbus-class "V-wing" starfighter, and the Eta-2 *Actis*-class light Interceptor. Like the much larger Star Courier, the V-wing and Interceptor had folding radiator wings, two ion engines, and laser cannons. Neither the V-wing nor the Interceptor had a built-in hyperdrive, but TransGalMeg Industries Inc. produced an attachable Syliure hyperdrive booster ring that enabled the Interceptor to travel through hyperspace. To maximize power for speed and agility, Kuat produced the starfighters without certain customary features: the Interceptor lacked energy shields, while the V-wing lacked a pressurized cockpit and required pilots to wear sealed flight suits equipped with life-support systems.

Raith Sienar incorporated the most economical features of Kuat Systems Engineering's Republic starfighters into a prototype for a more lethal and maneuverable twin ion engine fighter.

TIE FIGHTER PROTOTYPE

Imperial Navy records attest that several Imperial leaders, including Grand Moff Tarkin, believed the best way to prevent Imperial fighter pilots from deserting was to limit the pilots' range and ability to travel unassisted. Imperial admiralty agreed that Star Destroyers and other vessels should transport pilots and starfighters across space, while flight controllers within the carriers would be responsible for guiding the fighters in and out of the carriers' hangars. This operational plan would not only make Imperial starfighter pilots almost entirely dependent on their controllers, but also negated any need to equip the starfighter with a hyperdrive or landing gear.

To further reduce expenses and restrict the pilots' independence, Tarkin also advocated that the starfighter should be without energy-shield systems. Because energy shields protect pilots and passengers from radiation, micrometeoroids, and enemy laserfire, and because such shielding is a standard feature on almost every military, commercial, and civilian starship, Tarkin anticipated that some officers would contest or offer alternatives to his mandate. But Tarkin, a skilled pilot in his own right, noted that Jedi Generals had successfully piloted unshielded starfighters to defeat enemy droids during the Clone Wars, and posited that thoroughly trained Imperial pilots should have similar success with such starfighters against all opposition. Emperor Palpatine endorsed Tarkin's proposal, as they believed Imperial pilots, flying unshielded fighters, would be that much more committed to accomplishing their mission goals, and without any waste of time or energy.

After the Imperial Navy itemized their requirements and estimated the budget for developing and manufacturing the new starfighter, Raith Sienar began designing a prototype. As previously noted, Sienar incorporated design aspects from Kuat Systems Engineering's Alpha-3 *Nimbus*-class

◄ In keeping with the Imperial Navy's commission for a new starfighter designed exclusively for space combat, Raith Sienar's initial concept was without components and structural reinforcements necessary for atmospheric flight.

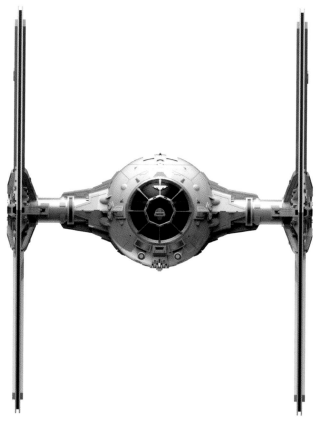

▲ A side view of the TIE fighter prototype, with its starboard wing removed, displays the port-side wing's inner solar collectors.

▲▼ Sienar added bulked-up wing spars to make the TIE fighter prototype flightworthy in atmospheres as well as space.

"V-wing" starfighter and Eta-2 *Actis*-class light Interceptor for the prototype Imperial twin ion engine starfighter. Working from Imperial directives, Sienar designed the initial prototype exclusively for space combat, and not for atmospheric-flight capability. But when Sienar presented his designs to Navy officials, he surprised them with an alternate design for a slightly more expensive starfighter. The alternate design featured stronger pylons within bulked-up spars that connected the wings to the cockpit module, an increase to overall structural integrity that would allow the fighter to travel through atmospheres and also the ability to land on its wings.

Impressed by Sienar's presentation, Navy officials authorized Sienar to construct prototypes for both proposed designs. After testing the prototypes, the Navy agreed that Sienar's alternate design was more practical, and that the additional expense would be a worthy investment.

PRODUCTION FACILITIES

During the Clone Wars, the Galactic Grand Army and the Confederacy of Independent Systems brought forth many innovations in the production of capital ships, starfighters, armor, and related weapons and defensive systems, but their combined output paled in comparison with the Galactic Empire's unprecedented advancements in manufacturing technologies. Emperor Palpatine spurred every scientist, engineer, technician, and laborer in Imperial space to not only participate in a united effort to build his new regime, but to be exceptionally productive. Imperial forces commandeered and refurbished all major starship yards and factories for the production of vehicles and weapons for the Imperial fleet.

To ensure that the costs for manufacturing TIE fighters would remain consistently low, Sienar Fleet Systems spared no expense on research, development, and design of a prototype for a TIE fighter production facility, which was in every way as vital to the Empire's goals as the TIE fighters

▲ TIE fighter components await assembly in an Imperial starship manufacturing facility on Corellia.

▼ Sprawling factory complexes produced countless TIE fighters during the Empire's occupation of Corellia.

By commissioning manufacturers to mass produce scores of TIE fighter cockpit pods and other components, the Empire prompted the revitalization of many antiquated Corellian factories.

The Imperial Navy conscripted skilled laborers on numerous worlds to help construct the Imperial fleet.

themselves. Raith Sienar mandated that the prototype factory would have the capability to process raw and prefabricated materials into functional components, and to automatically manufacture, assemble, and test every part for the TIE fighter, from the targeting computer to the solar-collecting wings.

By eliminating the need for technicians to run diagnostics or pilots to perform test flights before the TIE fighters left the factory, Sienar could guarantee to Grand Moff Tarkin that the factory would produce TIE fighters that were immediately ready for combat. SFS designers created the prototype factory using modular building materials that the Imperial Navy could produce, transport, and easily assemble at desired locations. After Imperial administrators approved the prototype factory, SFS provided Imperial engineers with blueprints for replicating the prototype, ensuring the Empire's ability to manufacture TIE fighters in abundance and without delay.

As the Emperor expanded his authority across space, Imperial administrators authorized the construction of new factories on any world that boasted a strategic location and sufficient resources, including metals, fuels, and dexterous

lifeforms that the Empire could conscript for manpower. Hence, factories on many worlds and orbital stations produced TIE fighters for the Empire, including factories on Corellia, Lothal, and Fondor.

IMPERIAL TIE FIGHTERS

Memorandum to Raith Sienar, Chief Executive Officer, Sienar Fleet Systems, from Grand Moff Tarkin, Regional Governor of the Outer Rim

"Just as the Grand Army of the Republic relied on starfighters to defend territories and to defeat the Separatists and their droid militias, the Empire requires starfighters to protect Imperial interests and engage our enemies. But unlike the Grand Army, the Imperial Army and Navy will be dealing with an opposition far more threatening than droids.

Our opposition will be lifeforms, including humans. And unlike droids, most lifeforms value their own existence, their own dreams, archaic beliefs, and traditions more than anything else. Already, populations of entire worlds have petitioned their grievances, and voiced their objections to becoming Imperial subjects. What the opposition seems unable to comprehend is that Imperial dominion is not a prospect, but a fate that the Emperor has already foreseen, and which the Emperor has entrusted me to actualize.

My mission is to educate such opposition, to make them comprehend the futility of challenging the Emperor's will. To accomplish this mission, I shall exploit the most common weakness that nearly all these lifeforms possess, the one thing that truly distinguishes them from machines. Their own emotions make them vulnerable, and their most crippling emotion is fear.

They fear change. They fear the unknown. They cannot imagine abandoning their selfish ways and superstitions in order to serve the Emperor as citizens of a unified galaxy. To maintain order and expand the Empire, the Imperial Army and Navy cannot give the opposition time to think or plan ahead. Those who refuse Imperial indoctrination must learn to fear the consequences of refusal. Emperor Palpatine has directed us to nurture that fear with firepower, and with the threat of even greater firepower.

If the opposition is not intimidated by the sight of our capital ships in planetary orbit, and if a barrage from Imperial cannons does not result in the opposition's immediate surrender, the Emperor envisions that we shall unleash swarms of starfighters that will seek out and destroy any survivors. Furthermore, the Emperor does not wish these Imperial starfighters to be silent as they race toward their targets, but that they shall release a noise akin to a screech from a bird of prey. The noise should startle our enemies, injecting instant terror into their veins. The noise will make them freeze behind the triggers and controls of their own weapons. The noise will be the last sound they hear before the starfighter opens fire.

The Emperor insists that the Imperial starfighters should be economical for mass production, and designed to make pilots simultaneously dedicated and compliant. And above all, the Emperor wants our starfighters to incite fear."

◀ Two Imperial TIE fighters, traveling toward the Death Star battle station, exhibit their respective twin ion engines as small points of red light on either side of a hexagonal solar ionization reactor.

TIE/in SPACE SUPERIORITY STARFIGHTER

After the Imperial Navy approved Raith Sienar's design for the TIE fighter, Sienar Fleet Systems began mass production of the craft in factories across the galaxy. The Empire's official name for the craft was the *Twin Ion Engine line edition space superiority starfighter*, which Sienar abbreviated as TIE/in. Production data remains classified, but according to numerous estimates, Sienar manufactured a minimum of approximately 4.6 million Imperial TIE fighters for Star Destroyers, other Imperial Naval vessels, and Imperial garrisons and defense stations. Most estimates maintain that more Imperial TIE fighters were operational at the same time than any other starfighter in history. Two SFS P-s3 ion engines powered the fighter, which could attain a maximum speed of 1,200 kilometers per hour in atmospheres. After initial production runs, Sienar replaced the P-s3 with the more efficient SFS P-s4. Although pilots depended on traffic controllers and automated tractor-beam projectors to move their TIE fighters in and out of starship hangars and docking bays, repulsorlift cyclers in the TIE/in's wing spars enabled vertical takeoff and landing in atmospheres. Because the TIE/in ion engine had no moving parts, the durable engine

seldom broke down during combat missions. According to Imperial Navy records, less than five percent of TIE losses were from field attrition, and the Navy attributed the majority of those losses to pilot error. Knowing that TIE fighters were more likely to be shot down than break down, TIE fighter pilots could concentrate on their mission objectives and targets without concern about whether their fighters' engines would fail.

▲ An Imperial TIE/in opens fire on a rebel X-wing starfighter near the Death Star at the Battle of Yavin.

◄ Scores of TIE fighters defended the shield gate, an Imperial space station in orbit of the planet Scarif.

▶ Sienar Fleet Systems engineered TIE fighters primarily for space combat and without landing gear, but made the craft capable of atmospheric flights and landing on its wings.

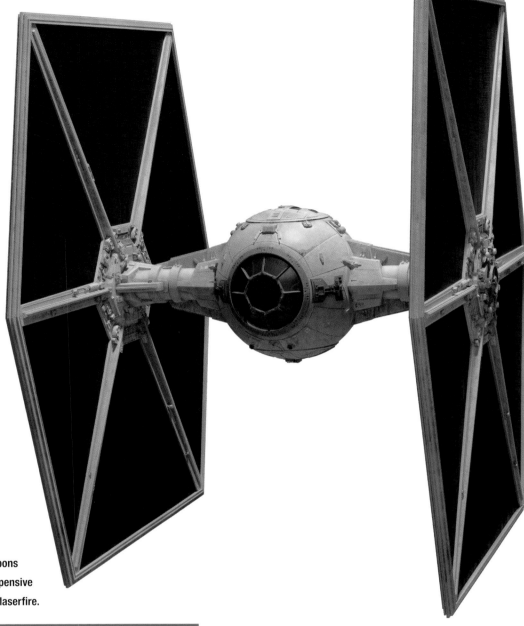

▼ Like most Imperial weapons of war, TIE fighters used expensive gases that produced green laserfire.

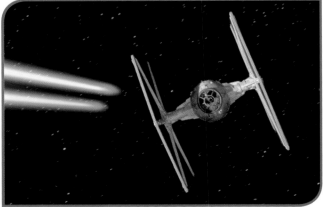

Sienar manufactured the TIE/in so that every fighter was identical, inside and out. Imperial technicians and mechanics followed strict procedures to ensure that each TIE was fully operational before leaving a hangar. As previously noted, the TIE fighter's lack of deflector shields reduced manufacturing costs and increased maneuverability, but the deficiency left the fighter vulnerable to direct hits from military lasers or heavy blasters. However, this very vulnerability motivated Imperial pilots to compensate by shooting first, making each shot count, and attacking in large numbers.

SPECIFICATIONS TIE/in SPACE SUPERIORITY STARFIGHTER

MANUFACTURER:
Sienar Fleet Systems
AFFILIATION:
Galactic Empire
MODEL: TIE/in space
superiority starfighter
CLASS: Starfighter
LENGTH: 7.2 m (23 ft 9 in)
WIDTH: 6.7 m (21 ft 11 in)
HEIGHT: 8.8 m (28 ft 11 in)

MAXIMUM ACCELERATION: 4,100 G
MEGALIGHT PER HOUR: 100
MAXIMUM SPEED (ATMOSPHERE): 1,200 kph
(746 mph)
ENGINE: SFS P-s4 twin ion engines
HYPERDRIVE: None
SHIELDING: None
NAVIGATION SYSTEM: N-s6 Navcon
TARGETING SYSTEMS: T-s8 targeting
computer

ARMAMENT: SFS L-s1 laser
cannons (2)
ESCAPE CRAFT: Ejector seat
CREW: Pilot (1)
LIFE SUPPORT: None
CONSUMABLES: 2 days
COST: 60,000 Imperial
credits new; 25,000 used
(military requisition charges)

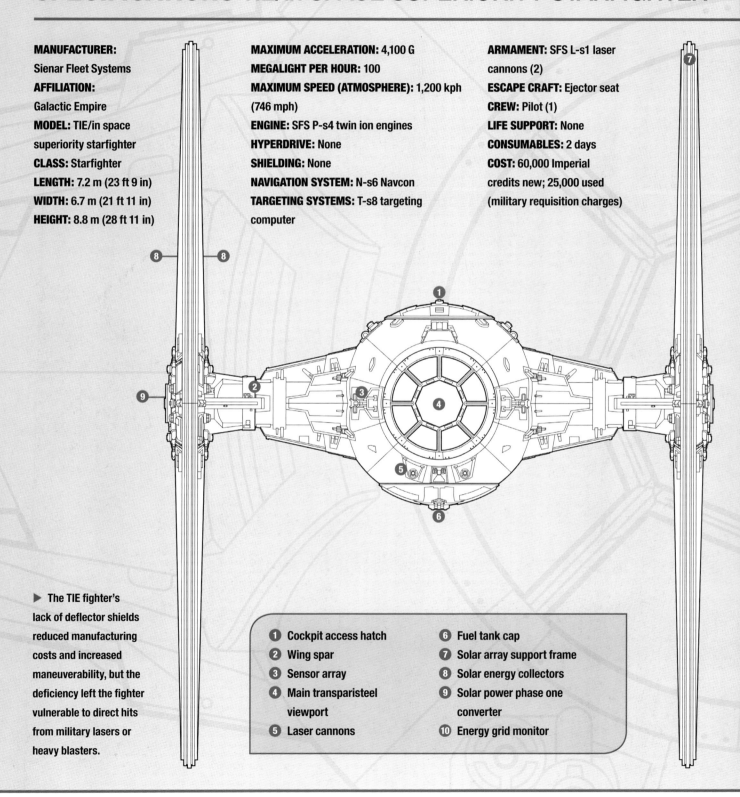

▶ The TIE fighter's
lack of deflector shields
reduced manufacturing
costs and increased
maneuverability, but the
deficiency left the fighter
vulnerable to direct hits
from military lasers or
heavy blasters.

1. Cockpit access hatch
2. Wing spar
3. Sensor array
4. Main transparisteel viewport
5. Laser cannons
6. Fuel tank cap
7. Solar array support frame
8. Solar energy collectors
9. Solar power phase one converter
10. Energy grid monitor

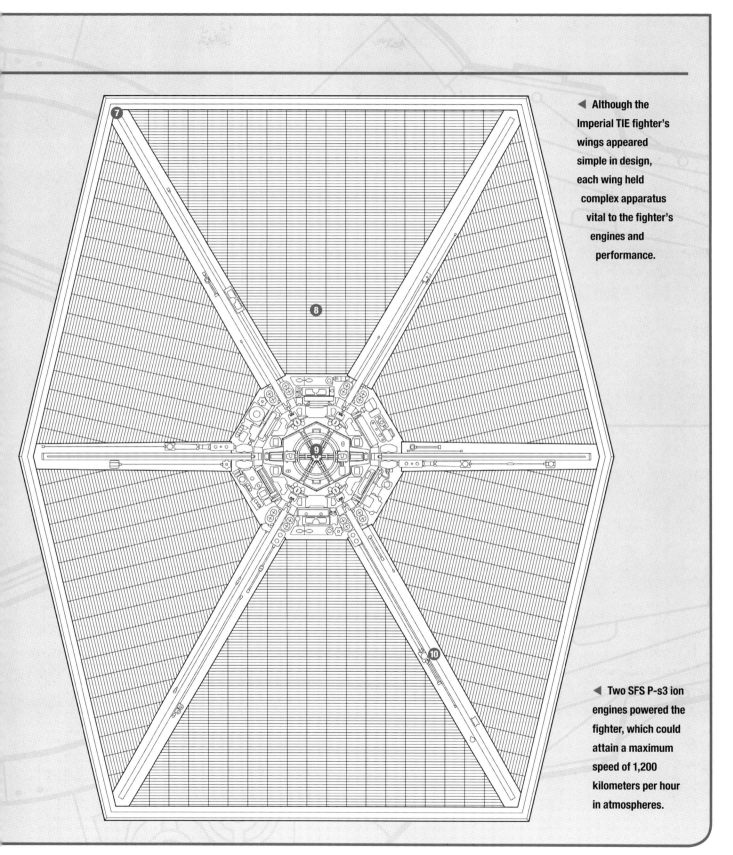

◀ Although the Imperial TIE fighter's wings appeared simple in design, each wing held complex apparatus vital to the fighter's engines and performance.

◀ Two SFS P-s3 ion engines powered the fighter, which could attain a maximum speed of 1,200 kilometers per hour in atmospheres.

VIEWS

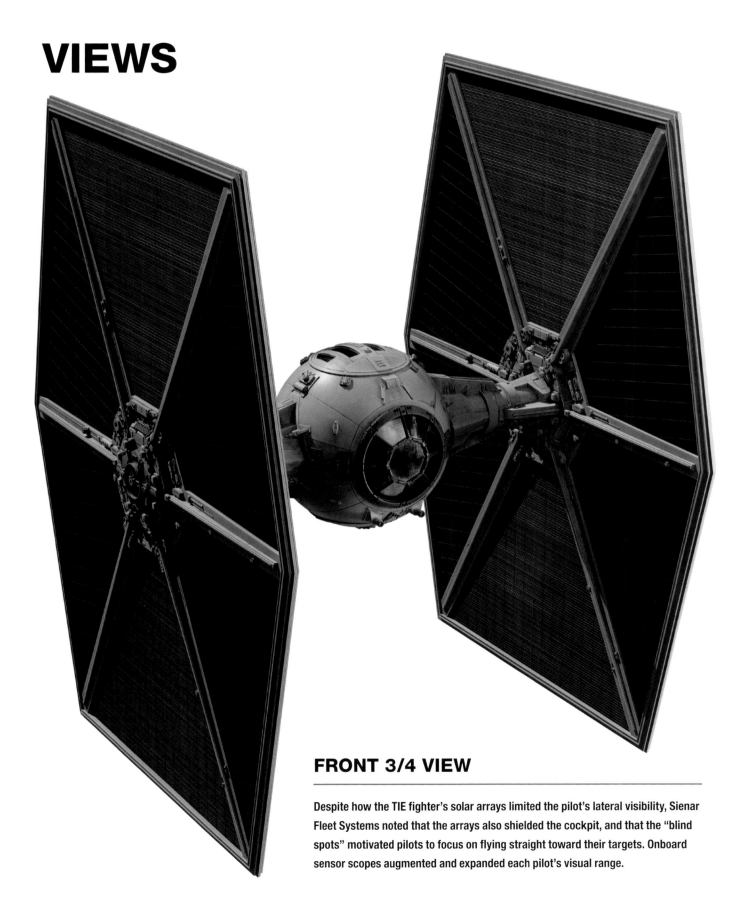

FRONT 3/4 VIEW

Despite how the TIE fighter's solar arrays limited the pilot's lateral visibility, Sienar Fleet Systems noted that the arrays also shielded the cockpit, and that the "blind spots" motivated pilots to focus on flying straight toward their targets. Onboard sensor scopes augmented and expanded each pilot's visual range.

DORSAL AND VENTRAL VIEWS

Located on top of the TIE fighter's cockpit pod, the cockpit access hatch held four thin transparisteel windows. Basic grips and locking mechanisms enabled pilots to use a single hand to open, close, and secure the hinged hatch. The hatch also served as the escape route for the pilot's ejector seat.

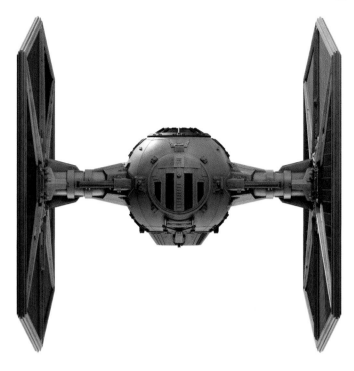

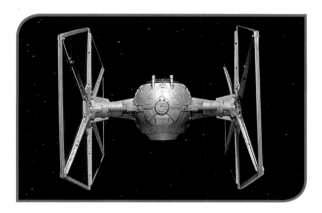

FORWARD AND AFT VIEWS

Rebel pilots routinely used the slang term "eyeballs" in reference to TIE fighters, as each TIE cockpit pod and viewport did indeed resemble a large eye. At the TIE cockpit pod's aft, Sienar Fleet Systems P-s4 twin ion engines were located on either side of an SFS I-a2b solar ionization reactor.

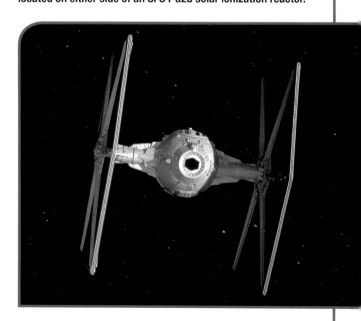

SOLAR-COLLECTOR WINGS

The standard Imperial TIE fighter had two hexagonal solar energy-collecting wings. Both sides of each wing had six trapezoidal solar arrays, which collected energy from distant and nearby stars, and converted that energy into power for the fighter's ion engines and—in early TIE fighter models—weapons. Rigid quadanium steel foil braces framed the solar arrays. Besides collecting solar energy, the wings also served as physical shields, offering limited lateral protection against enemy laserfire.

Working in his eponymous Advanced Projects Laboratory, Raith Sienar explored various design possibilities for the wings, including curved and angled shapes that would offer better aerodynamics in atmospheres, and also wider visibility for the pilot. Sienar determined that "bending" the wings at angles that inclined toward the cockpit module would help shield the pilot without substantial loss of energy-gathering capacity, and that some "bent wing" configurations enhanced maneuverability. He also explored concepts for modified wing spars and cockpit pods that could carry different weapons and payloads. However, Sienar also determined that such enhancements would cost more than the budget that the Navy had allocated for the TIE/in. After computers and flight simulators confirmed that the hexagonal wing configuration offered the most economic, energy efficient, and aerodynamically practical combination, Sienar knew that the Imperial Navy would readily accept the hexagonal wings for their new starfighter.

Although the solar-collecting wings on Sienar Fleet Systems' first TIE/in fighters powered the fighters' laser cannons as well as the ion engines, Imperial pilots soon discovered that firing the cannons repeatedly during heavy combat would divert critical energy from the ion engines and reduce maneuverability. Sienar retrofitted existing TIE/in fighters with a separate power generator for the laser cannons,

◀ **Sienar Fleet Systems packed the TIE fighter's connective wing spars with power lines and energy collection coils.**

▶ The TIE fighter's large viewport enabled TIE pilots to survey combat areas as they selected targets that posed the most immediate threat to Imperial ships or property.

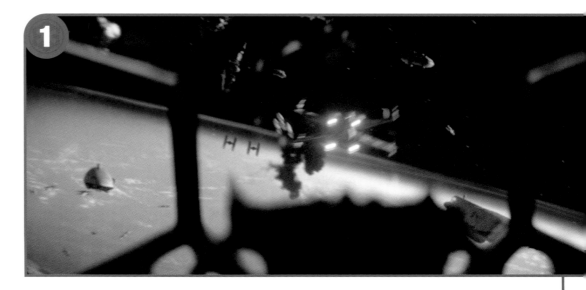

▶ As the TIE pilot engaged and closed in on an enemy craft, an illuminated rendering of the target appeared on the targeting computer's central screen.

▶ After the TIE fighter's targeting computer locked onto an enemy craft, the TIE pilot triggered the fighter's laser cannons to disable or destroy the craft.

ION ENGINE

Ion engines are a common type of sublight drive for starfighters and larger starships, used for traveling through realspace at speeds below the speed of light. Like other sublight drives, ion engines generate charged particles to propel the ship. Unlike other starship engines, ion engines have no moving parts and no high-temperature components. Thus, ion engines require less maintenance, a time and cost-saving factor that the Imperial Navy fully exploited.

While designing the Imperial TIE fighter's propulsion systems, Raith Sienar analyzed features of the twin ion engines used in Kuat Systems Engineering's Eta-2 *Actis-*class light interceptor, a starfighter used by Jedi Generals in the Clone Wars. The Eta-2 had a pressurized cockpit,

a Class 1 hyperdrive, and utilized an externally mounted astromech droid for inflight navigational support, maintenance, and emergency repairs. At the behest of the Jedi Council on Coruscant, the Eta-2 lacked energy shields, which allowed Kuat's engineers to dedicate substantially more energy to the Eta-2's engines and weapons. The Eta-2 had a maximum acceleration of 5,200G, and a maximum atmospheric speed of 1,500 kph.

As the Imperial Navy had assigned Sienar to design a short-range fighter, Sienar knew that a hyperdrive and astromech droid were unnecessary, and that a pilot wearing a pressurized flight suit would eliminate the need for the cockpit to have a built-in life-support system. Sienar also

REACTOR AND ENGINE SYSTEM

1. Reinforced exterior plating
2. Hi-energy plasma injectors
3. Exhaust neutralizer grid
4. Secondary power collector
5. Reactor housing
6. Focusing nodes
7. Fuel lines
8. Ion engine assembly
9. Solar power lines

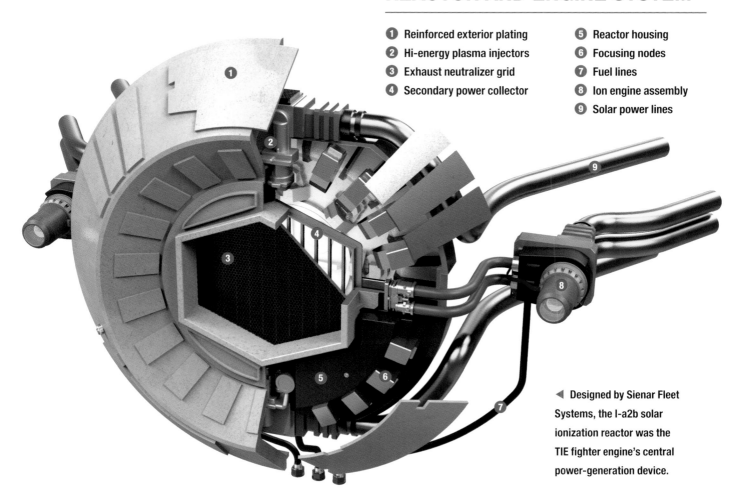

◄ Designed by Sienar Fleet Systems, the I-a2b solar ionization reactor was the TIE fighter engine's central power-generation device.

PORT ENGINE

1. Ion acceleration grids
2. Vectoring grids
3. Ionization chamber
4. Magnet ring
5. Control charge inputs
6. Particle energizer
7. Injector relay housing
8. Propellant pump
9. Solar power lines

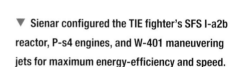

▼ Sienar configured the TIE fighter's SFS I-a2b reactor, P-s4 engines, and W-401 maneuvering jets for maximum energy-efficiency and speed.

knew, despite his selective appropriations of the Eta-2's features, that Kuat designed and customized the Eta-2 specifically for Jedi pilots, and that any attempt to replicate the Eta-2's speed or controls for human pilots would be almost entirely impractical.

Sienar Fleet Systems developed the SFS P-s3 ion engine specifically for the Imperial TIE fighter. With the P-s3, the Imperial TIE fighter had a maximum acceleration of 4,100G, and a maximum atmospheric speed of 1,200 kph. Sienar eventually replaced the P-s3 with the SFS P-s4, which offered 15 percent better fuel efficiency, and featured upgraded heat exchangers that were less prone to flux.

The Imperial TIE fighter's propulsion system accelerated ionized gases to a substantial fraction of lightspeed in microparticle accelerators. Emitted from the fighter's aft vents, the fast-moving particles streamed away from the fighter as they propelled the craft forward. Because TIE fighters used their propulsion mass extremely efficiently, they carried limited fuel supplies. At full power, the twin ion engines made the Imperial TIE fighter faster than most commercial spacecraft, and more than a match for most Rebel starfighters.

TIE STARFIGHTER SERIES

"The Imperial TIE fighter is arguably the clearest and most ubiquitous symbol of the Imperial Navy's control of space. TIE fighters escort fleets, provide reconnaissance, patrol disputed sectors of space, engage smugglers and pirates, and hunt down insurgents. TIE fighters are present aboard even the smallest Imperial cruisers, and are stationed at spaceports and garrison bases across the galaxy, an ever-present reminder of the Empire's might.

But if we are to achieve the Emperor's goals for expansion, we need more. And not just more TIE line edition starfighters, but variant fighters built for special purposes. For too long, we have relied on standard TIE fighters to perform on missions that would be better suited for long-range starfighters, or fighters built to carry heavier payloads. I can think of more than a dozen situations that Navy engineers attempted to modify TIE fighters into bombers, and I also recall more than a dozen failures. I do not mean to disparage our own engineers, but the fact is that the one individual who knows more about TIE fighters than anyone else is already under contract with the Navy, and I dare say we would be irresponsible if we did not commission him to help us meet our objectives. I'm speaking, of course, of Raith Sienar, Chief Executive Officer of Sienar Fleet Systems.

At Grand Moff Tarkin's direction, I met with Raith Sienar yesterday. I am pleased to report that Sienar has already given much thought to design possibilities for other starfighters and ancillary craft. In fact, and purely on speculation, he had already prepared concepts and rough schematics for a TIE bomber with a frame that may be useful for other craft. I am further pleased to report that Sienar's new concepts do not radically depart from his design for the TIE line edition, and that the concepts are immediately recognizable as fighters in what we might define as the TIE series.

And when citizens of the galaxy see this TIE *series* in action, they will know and have every reason to believe that Palpatine's Empire is only getting stronger."

—Imperial Navy Admiral Nils Tenant addressing the members of Imperial High Command and the Joint Chiefs of the Galactic Empire at [REDACTED]

◄ Deployed from an Imperial Star Destroyer, two TIE/in fighters bracket a TIE/in Interceptor as they advance in attack formation.

TIE/rb HEAVY STARFIGHTER (AKA TIE BRUTE)

As the Galactic Empire expanded into the lawless reaches of the Outer Rim, TIE fighter pilots began to routinely encounter vessels operated by pirates, smugglers, and criminal organizations. Because such enemy ships typically carried multiple laser cannons, and were equipped with hyperdrives that enabled swift escapes across space, a contingent of Imperial Navy admirals conscripted Sienar Fleet Systems to develop a new TIE fighter that would be better equipped to deal with Outer Rim malefactors. Before Sienar designers began work, Navy admiralty were already referring to the new TIE fighter as the *Infiltrator*.

Sienar responded with a prototype that they dubbed the TIE reinforcement battery heavy starfighter, or TIE/rb. Taller and wider than a standard TIE fighter, the TIE/rb featured heavier armor and greater firepower. Triple-laminate quadranium-reinforced titanium armor covered the command pod's exterior, and micro-corrugated solar panels provided additional protection to the wing arrays. An additional pod on the port-side wing spar housed an artillery battery of pivoting self-powered SFS H-s9.3 twin laser cannons, which had nearly twice the destructive capacity of the standard TIE fighter's L-s1 laser cannons.

The TIE/rb had a pressurized cockpit, which allowed the pilot to operate the fighter without wearing cumbersome helmets and pressure suits. Because the TIE/rb's size made it a larger target than a standard TIE fighter, and because SFS designers anticipated that enemy starships might concentrate assaults on the TIE/rb, the TIE/rb's viewport was made of extra-thick transparisteel. The pilot's seat was linked to an ejection system, but the seat differed from those found in standard TIE fighters in that a network of shock absorbers protected the pilot from bone-jarring jounces during dogfights and evasive maneuvers.

However, the weight of the TIE/rb's armor and weapons made the fighter substantially slower than its TIE/in counterpart when flying through atmospheres. Testing the TIE/rb prototype in flight simulators, most pilots agreed that the fighter could be dangerously sluggish. To help pilots adjust to the TIE/rb, SFS installed an MGK-300 integrated droid intelligence that provided inflight support. Operating in

◀ To protect Imperial interests in the mineral-rich planet Kessel, the Navy routinely used TIE/rb and TIE/in fighters to patrol the shifting systems of interstellar gas that surrounded the Kessel system.

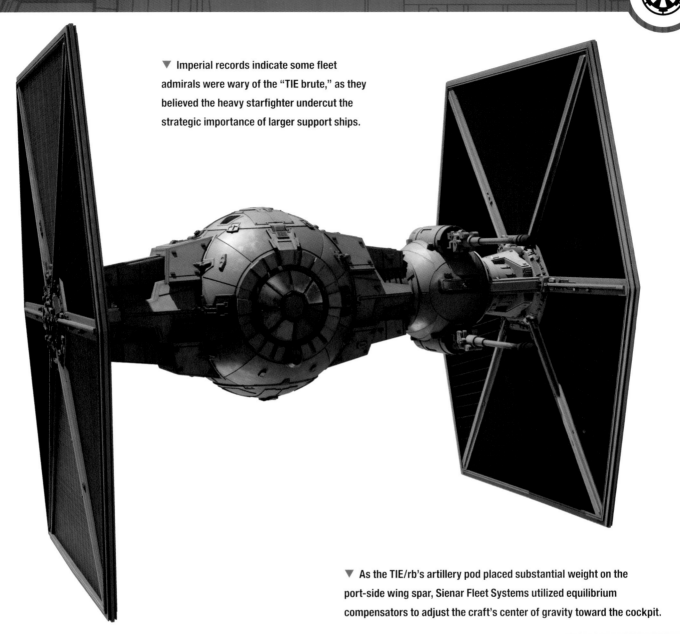

▼ Imperial records indicate some fleet admirals were wary of the "TIE brute," as they believed the heavy starfighter undercut the strategic importance of larger support ships.

▼ As the TIE/rb's artillery pod placed substantial weight on the port-side wing spar, Sienar Fleet Systems utilized equilibrium compensators to adjust the craft's center of gravity toward the cockpit.

a manner similar to an astromech droid, but without taking up valuable space within or outside the TIE/rb, the disembodied MGK-300 assisted with navigation and weapons systems, ran diagnostics, guided pilots toward targets, and alerted pilots to technical malfunctions, breaches, and other hazards.

Despite the TIE/rb's obvious advantages in certain combat scenarios, Imperial authorities, including influential fleet admirals, were wary of producing the fighter in large numbers because they believed it undercut the strategic importance of larger support ships. But the TIE/rb also had many proponents, especially among pilots who appreciated the fighter's remarkable durability and firepower. Imperial pilots nicknamed the starfighter the "TIE brute."

SPECIFICATIONS TIE/rb HEAVY STARFIGHTER

MANUFACTURER: Sienar Fleet Systems

AFFILIATION: Galactic Empire

MODEL: TIE/rb heavy starfighter

CLASS: Starfighter

LENGTH: 8.9 m (29 ft 3 in)

WIDTH: 12.2 m (40 ft)

HEIGHT: 11 m (36 ft 1 in)

MAXIMUM ACCELERATION: 2,300 G

MEGALIGHT PER HOUR: 90

MAXIMUM SPEED (ATMOSPHERE): 800 kph (500 mph)

ENGINE: SFS P-s4 twin ion engines

HYPERDRIVE: None

SHIELDING: Reinforced armor

NAVIGATION SYSTEM: MGK-300 droid (support)

TARGETING SYSTEMS: T-s8 targeting computer; MGK-300 droid (support)

ARMAMENT: SFS H-s9.3 twin laser cannons

ESCAPE CRAFT: Ejector seat

CREW: Pilot (1)

LIFE SUPPORT: Equipped

CONSUMABLES: 2 days

COST: 90,000 Imperial credits new; 40,000 used (military requisition charges)

▼ The expense of the TIE/rb's artillery pod and armor discouraged the Imperial Navy from producing the "brute" in larger numbers.

1. Cockpit access hatch
2. Wing spar
3. Sensor array
4. Main transparisteel viewport
5. Pivoting self-powered twin laser cannons
6. Fuel tank cap
7. Solar array support frame
8. Solar energy collectors
9. Solar power phase one converter
10. Energy grid monitor
11. Micro-corrugated solar-collecting panel
12. Triple-laminate quadranium-reinforced titanium armor
13. Optional gunner viewport

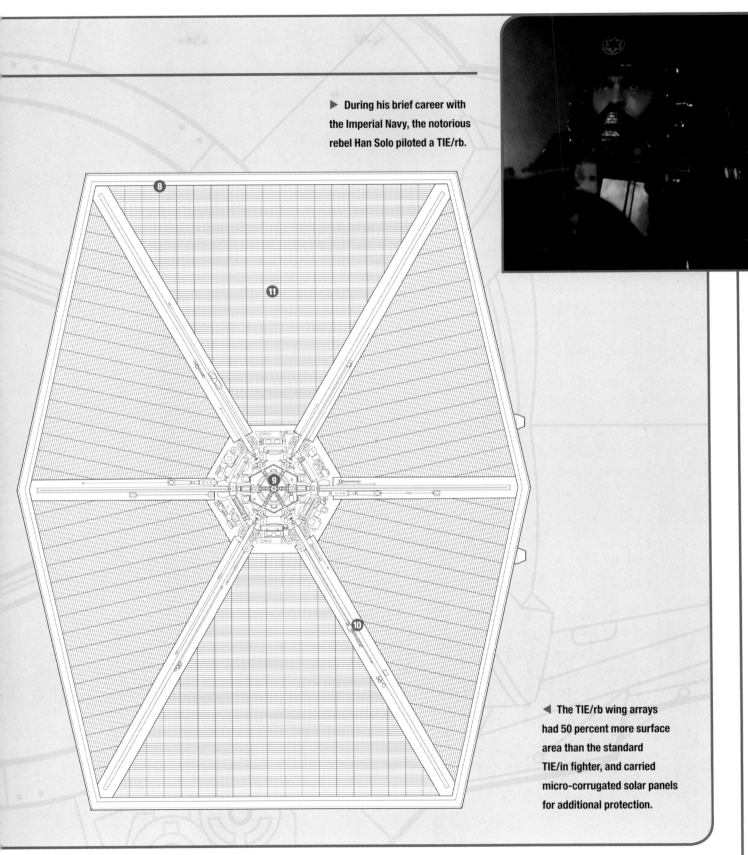

▶ During his brief career with the Imperial Navy, the notorious rebel Han Solo piloted a TIE/rb.

◀ The TIE/rb wing arrays had 50 percent more surface area than the standard TIE/in fighter, and carried micro-corrugated solar panels for additional protection.

TIE/sa BOMBER

During the rise of the Empire, the Imperial Navy relied on Imperial capital ships for space and orbital bombardment, and began using TIE/in fighters for the related tasks of bombing missions, including serving as ground support for long-range attacks, despite the fact that Sienar Fleet Systems had primarily designed and engineered the TIE fighter for short-range space combat. Although Star Destroyers could inflict massive damage and reduce targets to rubble, such destruction was undesirable and impractical when Imperials wanted to seize enemy bases and protect nearby resources. Navy officials eventually determined that a starfighter bomber would deliver warheads to space and planetary targets with greater accuracy and minimal wasted resources, and the Navy commissioned Sienar to design a prototype.

Sienar responded with the TIE Surface Assault Bomber, or TIE/sa, which was even more robust than the TIE/rb heavy starfighter. Structurally reinforced to survive the back-blast from bombardments during atmospheric strikes, the TIE bomber featured a pair of cylindrical pods positioned side-by-side between two "bent" wings. The solar panels on the bomber's wings provided a greater energy-collecting surface area than the standard TIE fighter, and were necessary for the bomber's power requirements.

The TIE bomber's starboard pod held a cockpit for a single pilot, and carried flight computers, power regulators, and communications gear. Because the Navy deployed bombers for longer missions than standard starfighters, the bomber had life-support systems that allowed the pilot to work without the constraints of a pressure suit, and carried a two-day supply of air and rations. The bomber was also one of the first Imperial starfighters equipped with an ejection seat. Because TIE bombers frequently operated in planetary atmospheres, where the pilot was more likely to find a survivable environment than if operating in deep space, and because TIE bomber pilots required more extensive training than TIE fighter pilots, the Imperial Navy concurred with the practicality of the Sienar-engineered ejection system.

The TIE bomber's port-side pod contained two bomb bays that carried a variety of ordnance, including concussion

◀ To flush out or destroy concealed targets on uncharted worlds or planetoids, TIE bombers increased the breadth of their destructive paths by operating in pairs.

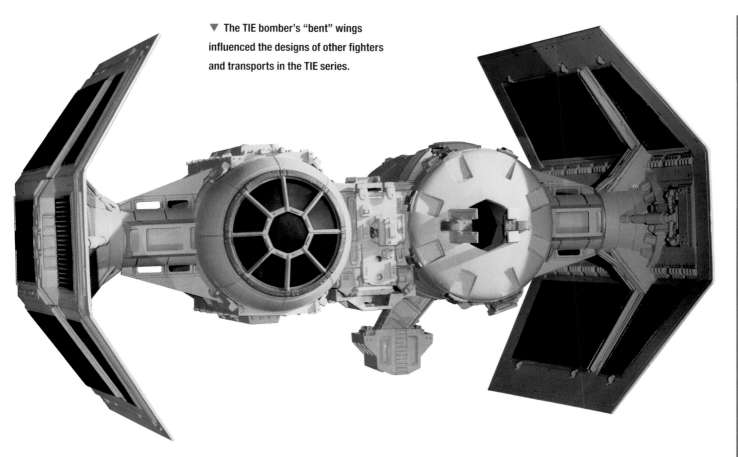

▼ The TIE bomber's "bent" wings influenced the designs of other fighters and transports in the TIE series.

missiles, orbital mines, and proton bombs. The port pod also housed a Nordoxicon-manufactured bomb sight, targeting sensors, beam altimeter, and several energy fuel cells. The bomber's weapons included two fire-linked laser cannons positioned below the cockpit on the starboard pod. Sienar developed the T-s7b targeting computer specifically for the bomber, and modified the computer for linkage to the ship's bomb sight.

The Navy soon came to depend on TIE bombers for surgical strikes. TIE bombers could conduct high-altitude or orbital bombing against ground targets, swoop down for low-level attacks, and operate alone, in pairs, or in squadrons. When the Navy coordinated bombing missions with standard TIE fighters, the bombers' long range and high payload proved even more dangerously effective.

▶ Because TIE bombers lacked hyperdrives, the Imperial Navy used hyperdrive-equipped starships, such as *Quasar Fire*-class cruiser-carriers, to transport TIE bombers to rebellious worlds and distant targets.

SPECIFICATIONS TIE/sa BOMBER

MANUFACTURER: Sienar Fleet Systems

AFFILIATION: Galactic Empire

MODEL: TIE/sa bomber

CLASS: Light bomber

LENGTH: 7.8 m (25 ft 7 in)

WIDTH: 9.3 m (30 ft 6 in)

HEIGHT: 5.1 m (16 ft 9 in)

MAXIMUM ACCELERATION: 2,380 G

MEGALIGHT PER HOUR: 90

MAXIMUM SPEED (ATMOSPHERE):
850 kph (528 mph)

ENGINE: SFS P-s4 twin ion engines

HYPERDRIVE: None

SHIELDING: Reinforced armor

NAVIGATION SYSTEM: N-s4 Navcon

TARGETING SYSTEMS: SFS T-s7b targeting computer (modified); Nordoxicon Micro Instruments 398X bomb sight

ARMAMENT: SFS L-s1 laser cannons (2); SFS M-s3 concussion missile and warhead launchers (2); various munitions

1 Cockpit access hatch	5 Laser cannons	9 Solar power phase one converter	12 Missile port
2 Wing spar	6 Fuel tank cap	10 Energy grid monitor	13 Bombadier viewport
3 Sensor array	7 Solar array support frame	11 Ordnance pod	14 Bombing chute
4 Main transparisteel viewport	8 Solar energy collectors		

ESCAPE CRAFT: Ejector seat
CREW: Pilot (1)
LIFE SUPPORT: Equipped
CONSUMABLES: 2 days
COST: 150,000 Imperial credits new;
60,000 used (military requisition charges)

▶ On Imperial warships, adjustable hangar racks accommodated TIE bombers as well as standard TIE fighters.

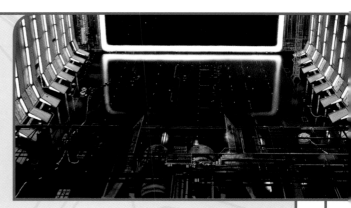

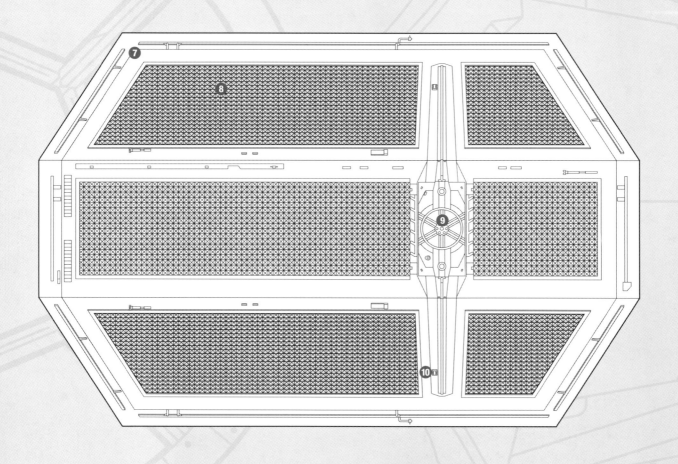

▲ For the TIE/sa bomber's cockpit pod, ordnance pod, and wing frames, Sienar Fleet Systems used the same quadranium steel-reinforced titanium armor materials that went into the TIE/rb heavy starfighter. But instead of incorporating the TIE/rb's micro-corrugated solar panels into the TIE bomber, Sienar created new panels that offered greater durability and energy efficiency.

TIE BOARDING CRAFT

After the Imperial Navy approved the TIE/sa bomber, the Navy commissioned Sienar Fleet Systems to design an armored shuttle that could transport a squad of stormtroopers from an Imperial Star Destroyer to other vessels or stations. The shuttle would also allow troopers to quickly board captured or disabled ships, and to recover Imperial or enemy escape pods. By various accounts, Navy officials proposed that Sienar should repurpose a TIE bomber as a boarding craft, as the officials believed building a prototype would require little more than modifying the bomber's ordnance pod into a compartment for passengers, and installing a docking hatch, retractable boarding ramp, and retractable landing gear. Sienar designers explained that repurposing an existing bomber would compromise its structural integrity, but appeased the Navy with a design for a boarding craft that was similar in overall appearance to a TIE bomber.

The resulting TIE boarding craft had a smaller transparisteel cockpit window and shorter length than the TIE bomber, but shared the same engine, sensor array, targeting computer, and other technological components. Both the starboard and port-side pods contained seats for six passengers, and

wall- and ceiling-mounted handgrips served to help standing passengers maintain their balance. The boarding craft's docking hatch was shielded by hinged armor plating, and equipped with a military-grade laser cutter. Sienar engineered the hinged armor plating to flare open and clamp onto a captured ship, and the laser cutter to create a large hole through the ship's hull or locked hatches. Stormtroopers typically used the boarding craft's retractable ramp when deploying on landing pads or planetary surfaces, and used the docking hatch as a hull-cutting airlock to board directly into enemy vessels.

Officials from the Commission for the Preservation of the New Order (COMPNOR), the Imperial government agency responsible for the promotion of New Order ideology, readily adopted the TIE boarding craft into service for one of their own divisions: the Imperial Office of Customs, which functioned to ensure that all commercial importers and exporters operated in full compliance with Imperial laws and regulations. Imperial Customs agents, accompanied by stormtrooper squads, routinely used TIE boarding craft to access freighters, inspect cargoes, and maintain authority.

◀ Although the Imperial Navy was first to adopt the TIE boarding craft, the vessel gained wider attention through its association with Imperial Customs agents, who operated from bases and stations on nearly every Imperial world.

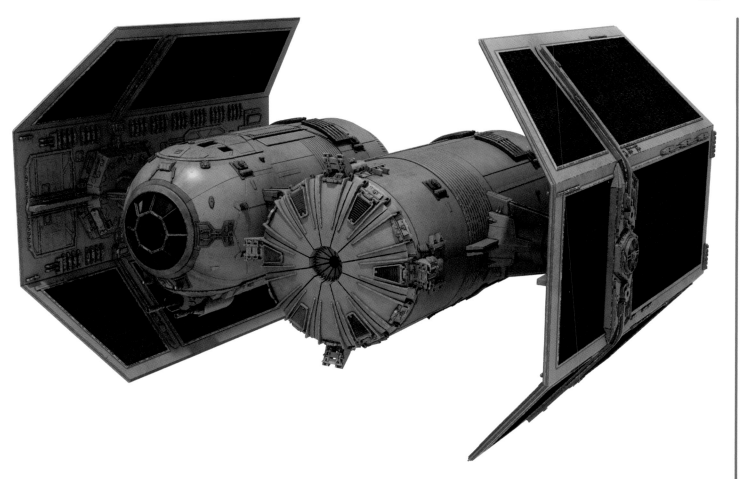

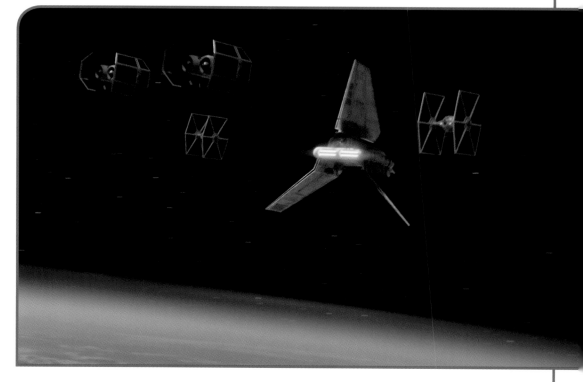

▲ The front of the TIE
boarding craft's port-side
pod was essentially a large,
retractable docking claw
with a hull-cutting laser that
enabled stormtrooper squads
to breach and rush into
enemy ships.

▶ TIE boarding crafts,
TIE/in fighters, and a Sienar
Fleet Systems Imperial
Lambda-class T-4a shuttle
assume an attack formation
to pursue an enemy starship.

SPECIFICATIONS TIE BOARDING CRAFT

MANUFACTURER: Sienar Fleet Systems

AFFILIATION: Galactic Empire

MODEL: Twin ion engine boarding craft

CLASS: Shuttle

LENGTH: 7.6 m (24 ft 11 in)

WIDTH: 9.9 m (32 ft 5 in)

HEIGHT: 5.9 m (19 ft 6 in)

MAXIMUM ACCELERATION: 2,380 G

MEGALIGHT PER HOUR: 90

MAXIMUM SPEED (ATMOSPHERE):
850 kph (528 mph)

ENGINE: SFS P-s4 twin ion engines

HYPERDRIVE: None

SHIELDING: Equipped

NAVIGATION SYSTEM: N-s4 Navcon

TARGETING SYSTEMS: T-s8 targeting
computer

ARMAMENT: L-s1 laser cannons (2); H-s1
heavy laser cannons (2); missile and
warhead launchers; various munitions

ESCAPE CRAFT: Ejector seat

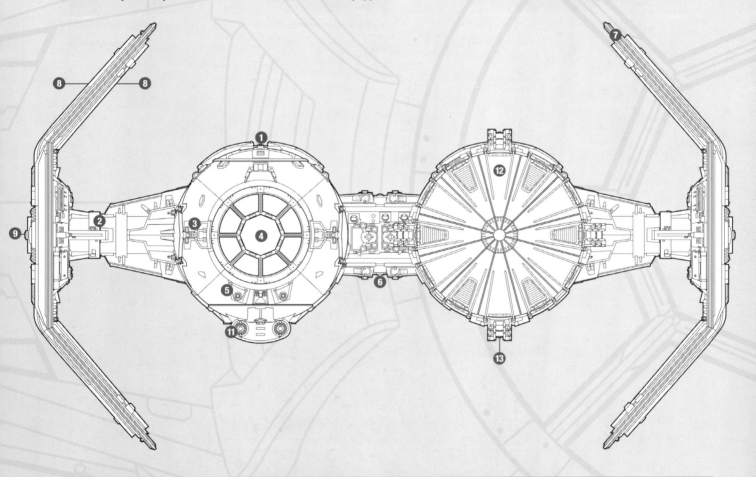

1. Cockpit access hatch
2. Wing spar
3. Sensor array
4. Main transparisteel viewport
5. Laser cannons
6. Fuel tank cap
7. Solar array support frame
8. Solar energy collectors
9. Solar power phase one converter
10. Energy grid monitor
11. Heavy laser cannons
12. Docking hatch and laser cutter
13. Retractable ramp

CREW: Pilot (1)

PASSENGERS: 20 (2 stormtrooper squads)

LIFE SUPPORT: Equipped

CONSUMABLES: 2 days

COST: 150,000 Imperial credits new; 60,000 used (military requisition charges)

▶ Despite an overall resemblance to the TIE/sa bomber, the TIE boarding craft was slightly taller and wider than the bomber, but shorter in length.

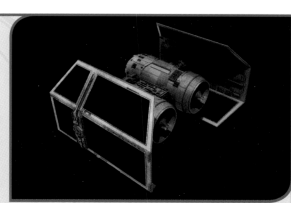

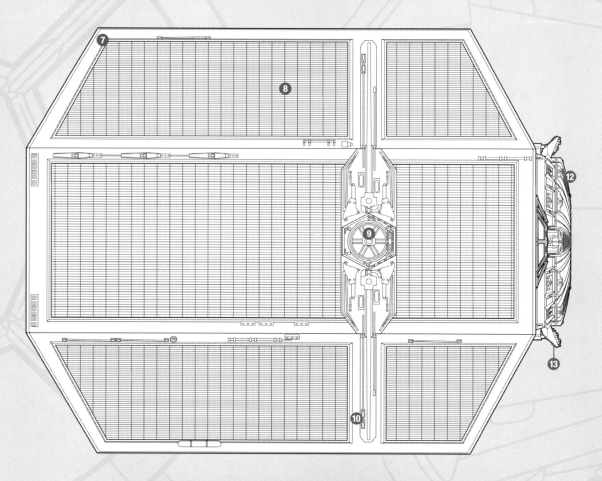

▲ The combination of an armored hull, energy shield projectors, and wing arrays with micro-corrugated solar panels served to protect the TIE boarding craft's passengers against enemy starfighters and pirate ships. Because the TIE boarding craft's main viewport extended slightly beyond the front of the wings, the craft offered greater visibility for the pilot than previous TIE models.

TIE COMMAND SHUTTLE

In their schematics for the Death Star, Imperial designers and engineers conceived an extensive matrix of interconnected turbolift tubes to convey passengers across the vast distances within the immense superweapon. However, during the Death Star's construction, Imperial Navy officials routinely used small shuttles to traverse the battle station, and also came to realize that such shuttles were also useful for traveling between Star Destroyers. At the Navy's behest, Sienar Fleet Systems converted a number of TIE bombers into shuttles by retrofitting ordinance pods with passenger cabins, but the bomber-shuttle conversions were purely utilitarian, more suitable for construction and technical crews than for high-ranking Navy officers. The Navy commissioned Sienar to design a distinctive command shuttle that would befit visiting Imperial dignitaries as well as Naval commanding officers.

Declassified data recordings reveal Naval officials were chagrined when Sienar responded that the top members of the Empire's hierarchy, which included Emperor Palpatine himself, had already commissioned Sienar to design an executive shuttle: the *Lambda*-class T-4a. The officials

were further vexed when their superiors informed them that the budget allocated for the *Lambda* shuttle would severely limit funding for the command shuttle.

Undeterred by budgetary concerns, Sienar responded with a solution, a prototype that was as practical as it was economical. Sienar modified an existing TIE bomber-shuttle conversion with a more luxurious passenger cabin, and 'flipped' the craft's solar-collecting wings to angle out and away from the vessel. Naval officials acknowledged that the flipped-wing configuration distinguished the shuttle from the TIE bomber, and agreed that Sienar's modified cabin interior was a great improvement on the previous utilitarian model.

Passengers could access the TIE Command Shuttle by either a retractable ramp or docking hatch. Although Imperials only used the shuttle for short journeys, the shuttle's amenities included padded seats, refrigerated food and drinks, and a refresher. In the unlikely event that the shuttle's crew and passengers would be required to defend themselves while traveling from an Imperial warship to a nearby station or spaceport, Sienar also equipped the shuttle with laser cannons and deflector shields.

◀ High-ranking Imperial officers and dignitaries, including the Emperor's lieutenant Darth Vader, routinely communicated via holographic transmissions, and reserved TIE Command Shuttles for important face-to-face meetings.

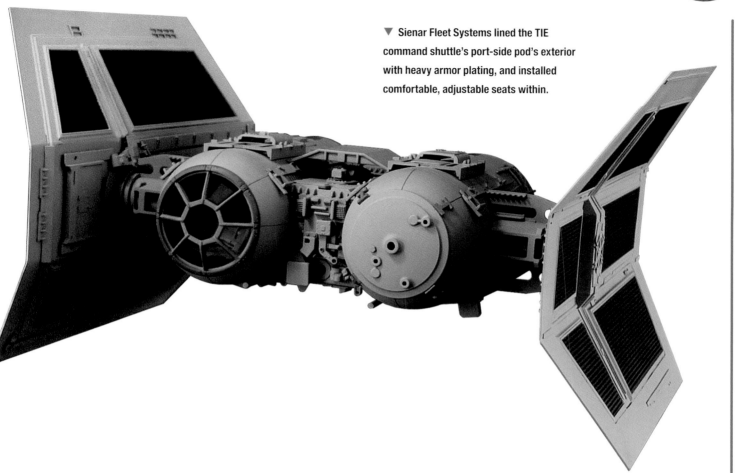

▼ Sienar Fleet Systems lined the TIE command shuttle's port-side pod's exterior with heavy armor plating, and installed comfortable, adjustable seats within.

► The TIE command shuttle was capable of atmospheric flight and planetary landings, but Navy officers more often used the craft to travel between Star Destroyers.

SPECIFICATIONS TIE COMMAND SHUTTLE

MANUFACTURER:
Sienar Fleet Systems

AFFILIATION: Galactic Empire

MODEL: Twin ion engine command shuttle

CLASS: Shuttle

LENGTH: 7.8 m (25 ft 7 in)

WIDTH: 10.4m (34 ft 1 in)

HEIGHT: 5.1 m (16 ft 9 in)

MAXIMUM ACCELERATION: 2,380 G

MEGALIGHT PER HOUR: 90

MAXIMUM SPEED (ATMOSPHERE):
850 kph (528 mph)

ENGINE: SFS P-s4 twin ion engines

HYPERDRIVE: None

SHIELDING: Equipped

NAVIGATION SYSTEM: N-s4 Navcon

TARGETING SYSTEMS: T-s8 targeting computer

ARMAMENT: Laser cannons (2)

ESCAPE CRAFT: Ejector seat

CREW: Pilot (1)

PASSENGERS: 12

LIFE SUPPORT: Equipped

CONSUMABLES: 2 days

COST: 150,000 Imperial credits new; 60,000 used (military requisition charges)

1 Cockpit access hatch
2 Wing spar
3 Sensor array
4 Main transparisteel viewport

5 Laser cannons
6 Fuel tank cap
7 Solar array support frame
8 Solar energy collectors

9 Solar power phase one converter
10 Energy grid monitor
11 Deflector shield generators

12 Docking hatch
13 Retractable ramp

▶ With a width greater than both the TIE/sa bomber and TIE boarding craft, the TIE command shuttle is a tight fit in hangars designed for similar twin-pod TIE craft so it usually docked in hangars reserved for officers.

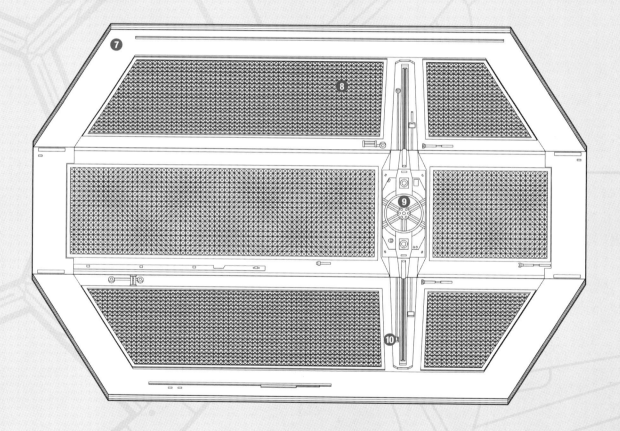

▲ Because Imperial officers insisted that the TIE Command Shuttle should match the speeds of the TIE/sa bomber and TIE boarding craft, and also that the shuttle should be equipped with deflector-shield generators, Sienar Fleet Systems constructed the shuttle with armored plating that was significantly lighter in weight than the plating used for similar Imperial TIE models, but entirely sufficient for a craft protected by deflector shields.

TIE ADVANCED v1

Fifteen years after the formation of the Galactic Empire, Imperial leaders unveiled Sienar Advanced Projects Laboratory's prototype for a new starfighter at the Capital City Empire Day parade on the planet Lothal. Sienar dubbed the fighter the TIE Advanced v1.

Drawing inspiration from the Eta-2 *Actis*-class light interceptor flown by Galactic Republic pilots during the Clone Wars, Sienar designers incorporated S-foils, also known as Strike foils, into the v1's wings. During normal flight, the v1's S-foils folded and locked in a closed position that brought the wings' upper and lower edges close to the cockpit module. When engaged in combat, pilots unlocked and opened the S-foils into an attack position. Sienar designed the folding wings to conserve space within TIE fighter hangars, and to give the v1 a top atmospheric speed of 1,600 kph, a significant increase over a standard TIE fighter's 1,200 kph.

Unlike other TIE fighters, the v1 had solar collectors on the inside of its wings, but not on the outside. Instead, heavy armor plating covered the wings' outside surfaces. Although the v1's high-performance solar collectors gathered more energy per square millimeter than solar collectors on standard TIE fighters, the v1's total solar-collecting capability was comparatively less, but provided sufficient power for the v1's less energy-intensive systems, and kept the fighter fully charged in most field conditions.

The v1's P-s5.2 twin ion engines and L-s9.1 laser cannons were more powerful than those found on a standard TIE fighter. Sienar also outfitted the v1 with basic deflector shields, advanced targeting systems, a projectile launcher, and a full life-support system that enabled the pilot to operate the craft without a pressurized suit and helmet. The projectile launcher's magazine carried up to 20 missiles, and could also deliver sophisticated tracking devices, such as the Imperial XX-23 S-Thread Tracers, to targeted vessels.

Sienar produced a small number of the TIE Advanced v1 prototype for the Inquisitors, an Imperial organization of Force-sensitive Jedi hunters. Despite the Inquisitors' powers and piloting skills, Rebel agents destroyed or captured most of the v1 prototypes.

◀ As both allies and enemies associated the Jedi-hunting Inquisitor with this TIE Advanced v1 prototype, the craft came to be commonly known as 'the Inquisitor's TIE Advanced.'

▲ With high-performance solar collectors inside the wings, and heavy armor plating on the outside, the TIE Advanced v1 was truly an advancement over the standard TIE/in fighter.

▶ Like the Clone Wars-era Eta-2 *Actis*-class light interceptor, the TIE Advanced v1's wings folded inward as the craft touched down on landing decks.

SPECIFICATIONS TIE ADVANCED v1

MANUFACTURER: Sienar Fleet Systems

AFFILIATION: Galactic Empire

MODEL: Experimental twin ion engine space superiority fighter

CLASS: Starfighter

LENGTH: 3.2 m (10 ft 4 in)

WIDTH: 6.6 m (21 ft 9 in)

HEIGHT: 5.7 m (18 ft 8 in)

MAXIMUM ACCELERATION: 4,150 G

MEGALIGHT PER HOUR: 105

MAXIMUM SPEED (ATMOSPHERE): 1,600 kph (994 mph)

ENGINE: SFS P-s5.2 twin ion engines

HYPERDRIVE: Class 4.5

SHIELDING: Equipped

NAVIGATION SYSTEM: N-s6.a Navcon

TARGETING SYSTEMS: T-s8.a targeting computer

ARMAMENT: L-s9.1 laser cannons (2); projectile launcher

ESCAPE CRAFT: Ejector seat

CREW: Pilot (1)

LIFE SUPPORT: Equipped

CONSUMABLES: 2 days

COST: 150,000 credits

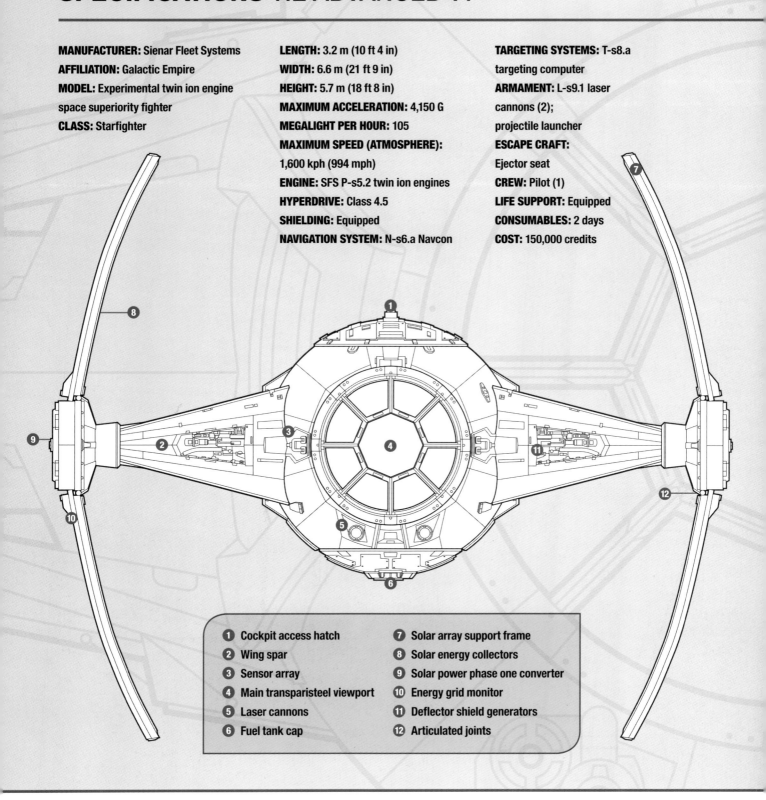

1. Cockpit access hatch
2. Wing spar
3. Sensor array
4. Main transparisteel viewport
5. Laser cannons
6. Fuel tank cap
7. Solar array support frame
8. Solar energy collectors
9. Solar power phase one converter
10. Energy grid monitor
11. Deflector shield generators
12. Articulated joints

▶ Sienar Fleet Systems engineered the TIE Advanced v1 to rest on its wings in either folded or unfolded configurations.

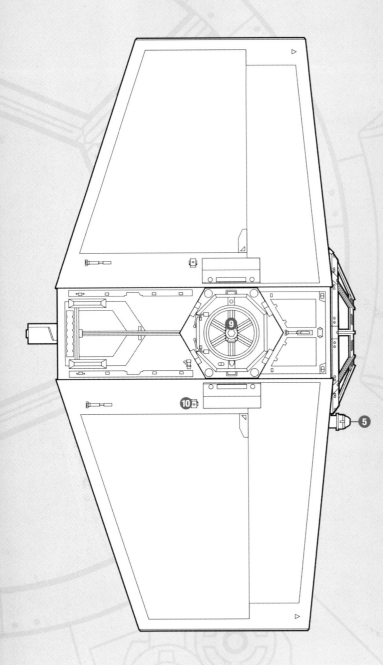

▲ After test flights in space and in atmospheres confirmed the TIE Advanced v1 prototype was faster, more maneuverable, and far more lethal than the standard TIE/ in fighter, Sienar Fleet Systems expected the Imperial Navy would want to begin mass production immediately. But after a string of setbacks involving Rebel agents on Lothal, the Navy put the TIE Advanced v1 on hold indefinitely.

TIE ADVANCED x1

Imperial officers and government leaders were unwaveringly dedicated to Emperor Palpatine, but declassified reports reveal numerous Imperials secretly bristled when assignments brought them under the command of the Emperor's mysterious and often intimidating apprentice Darth Vader, the Dark Lord of the Sith. Few people knew that Vader was formerly a Jedi Knight named Anakin Skywalker, who served as a General of the Grand Army of the Republic in the Clone Wars, and gained a legendary reputation for his exploits as a combat pilot.

While Imperial authorities may have wondered why the Emperor insisted on having Vader oversee certain operations, they knew better than to question orders from either the Emperor or Vader. When Vader directed Sienar Fleet Systems to develop a design for a new TIE fighter that would meet

his own personal specifications, SFS complied with total commitment, as if their client were the Emperor himself.

Vader's specifications included experimental protective energy shield projectors, a hyperdrive, a sophisticated target-tracking system, improved weapons, a reinforced hull with extra durasteel armor plating, and high-conversion solar cells on a "bent wing" configuration that would enable an augmented engine assembly, and also increase speed and maneuverability. SFS engineers were impressed by Vader's knowledge of technological systems, specifically his concepts for shield projectors and the engine. SFS designated the new fighter the TIE Advanced x1 Prototype.

The inclined wings collected more ambient energy to compensate for the additional mass, and to maintain the TIE's speed and agility in space. Non-standard Sienar Fleet

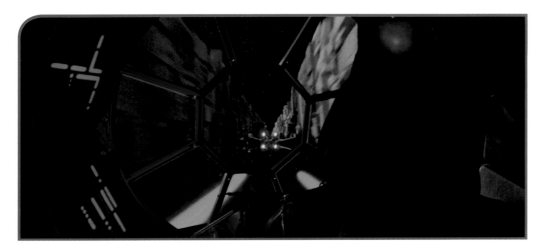

◀ The x1 prototype's cutting-edge Glucon CRX-9 targeting computer automatically adjusted to the pilot's own reaction times, but Darth Vader often used his own Force powers to locate and target enemy vessels.

◀ Darth Vader required the life-support systems in his suit and helmet to stay alive, but atmospheric controls in the x1 prototype's cockpit allowed him the option of removing his helmet for brief periods while operating the craft.

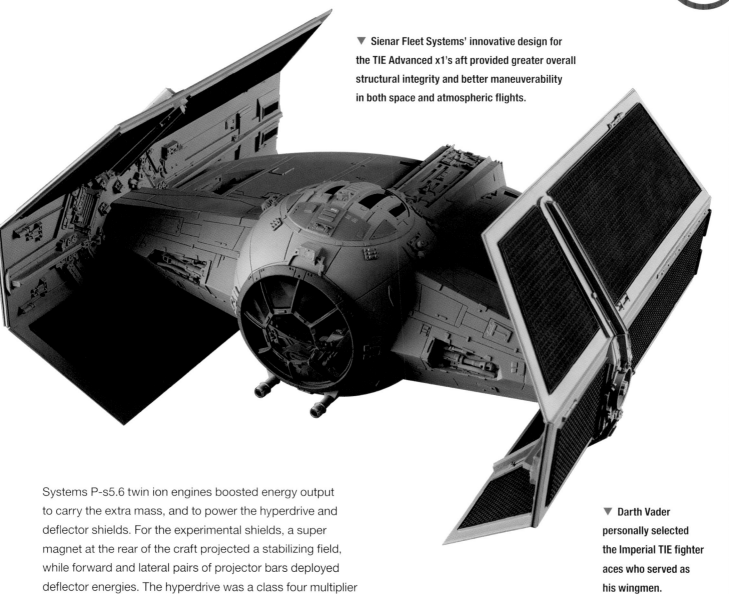

▼ Sienar Fleet Systems' innovative design for the TIE Advanced x1's aft provided greater overall structural integrity and better maneuverability in both space and atmospheric flights.

▼ Darth Vader personally selected the Imperial TIE fighter aces who served as his wingmen.

Systems P-s5.6 twin ion engines boosted energy output to carry the extra mass, and to power the hyperdrive and deflector shields. For the experimental shields, a super magnet at the rear of the craft projected a stabilizing field, while forward and lateral pairs of projector bars deployed deflector energies. The hyperdrive was a class four multiplier equipped with a non-droid-assisted navicomputer that stored coordinates for ten jumps in its memory for quick escapes into hyperspace.

Elite Imperial Navy fighter squadrons tested the limited-run x1 prototypes in field trials, and most pilots praised the craft's performance. Although the great expense of the x1 precluded Imperial authorities from considering mass production, SFS incorporated various x1 features—including high-performance solar cells and bent wings—into the next generation of full-production TIE fighters, the TIE Interceptors.

Because only Darth Vader and select Imperial pilots flew TIE Advanced x1 prototypes, enemies of the Empire regarded the prototypes as the most dangerous starfighters in the Imperial Navy.

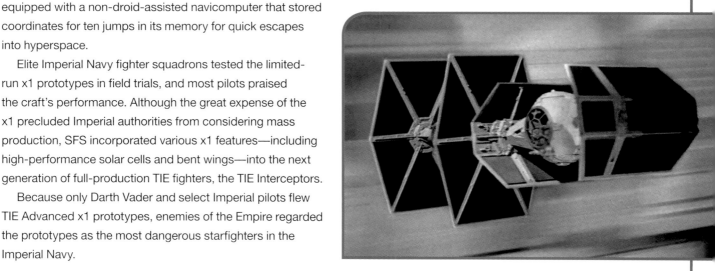

SPECIFICATIONS TIE ADVANCED x1

MANUFACTURER: Sienar Fleet Systems

AFFILIATION: Galactic Empire

MODEL: TIE Advanced x1 prototype

CLASS: Starfighter

LENGTH: 5.8 m (19 ft)

WIDTH: 6.2 m (20 ft 6 in)

HEIGHT: 3.8 m (12 ft 7 in)

MAXIMUM ACCELERATION: 4,150 G

MEGALIGHT PER HOUR: 105

MAXIMUM SPEED (ATMOSPHERE): 1,200 kph (746 mph)

ENGINE: SFS P-s5.6 twin ion engines

HYPERDRIVE: Class 4

SHIELDING: Equipped

NAVIGATION SYSTEM: Equipped, ten-jump limit

TARGETING SYSTEMS: Glucon CRX-9 targeting computer

ARMAMENT: L-s9.3 laser cannons (2)

ESCAPE CRAFT: Ejector seat

CREW: Pilot (1)

LIFE SUPPORT: Equipped

CONSUMABLES: 5 days

COST: 160,000 Imperial credits new; 65,000 used (military requisition charges)

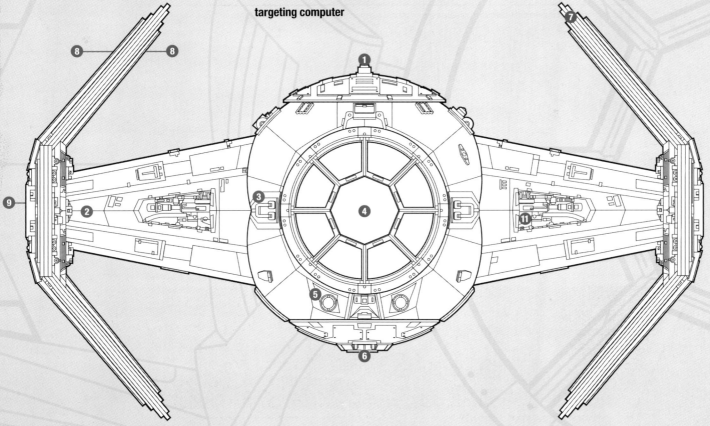

❶ Cockpit access hatch	❹ Main transparisteel viewport	❼ Solar array support frame	❿ Energy grid monitor
❷ Wing spar	❺ Laser cannons	❽ Solar energy collectors	⓫ Deflector shield
❸ Sensor array	❻ Fuel tank cap	❾ Solar power phase one converter	generators

▶ Like all Imperial TIE fighters, the TIE Advanced x1 was vulnerable to projectile weapons and collisions with large objects, but experimental energy shield projectors protected the x1 from heavy laserfire and micrometeoroids.

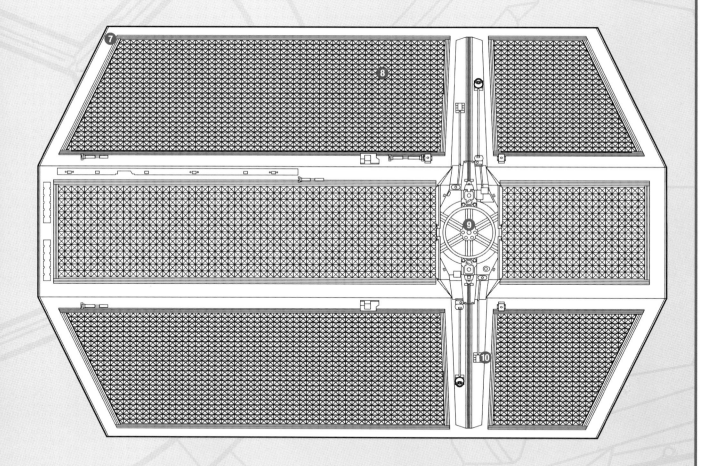

▲ Darth Vader gave specific instructions to Sienar Fleet Systems on the components and construction of the TIE Advanced x1's wings, which held high-conversion solar cells that enabled the craft's augmented engine assembly.

TIE/mg MINING GUILD

Although space pilots and citizens of the galaxy came to universally recognize the Sienar Fleet Systems TIE fighter as not just a starfighter but as a symbol of Imperial power, the Galactic Empire authorized a few business affiliates and planetary forces to use TIEs, albeit with certain restrictions. One such affiliate was the Mining Guild, a network of miners that harvested natural resources in numerous sectors throughout the galaxy.

Operating in concert with the Empire, the Mining Guild supplied Imperial forces with various raw materials and gases, including the gas Clouzon-36, which the Mining Guild refined into fuel for starships. After anti-Imperial agents stole substantial quantities of Clouzon-36 in a series of raids on Mining Guild facilities, representatives of the Mining Guild and the Imperial Navy met to discuss how they could collaborate against the thieving agents. The Navy agreed to provide the Mining Guild with TIE fighters for use as armed patrol ships, but only in the Mining Guild's established jurisdictions. The Navy also agreed to provide training for Mining Guild pilots to operate the TIE fighters. In exchange, the Mining Guild guaranteed regular supplies of Clouzon-36 to the Navy.

Spaceport authorities could easily distinguish the TIE/mg Mining Guild TIE starfighter by its yellow color scheme, and also by what resembled a notch cut into the fore sections of both wings. The distinctive 'notch' was the result of Sienar Fleet Systems constructing each wing to hold only four trapezoidal solar arrays on each side, or eight arrays per wing, instead of the requisite 12 arrays per wing on the standard Imperial TIE fighter. Because the Mining Guild TIE fighter's deliberately 'missing' arrays offered relatively less surface area for the armored wings to gather solar energy and protect the cockpit module, the fighter was not only less powerful than its Imperial counterpart but left the pilot more vulnerable to enemy fire. However, Mining Guild pilots appreciated that the 'notches' in the wings offered a wider range of visibility, and that the mere sight of their TIE fighters routinely encouraged enemy factions to surrender or retreat.

◀ **Like their Imperial counterparts, Mining Guild pilots typically flew in pairs or groups when patrolling areas around mining operations and facilities.**

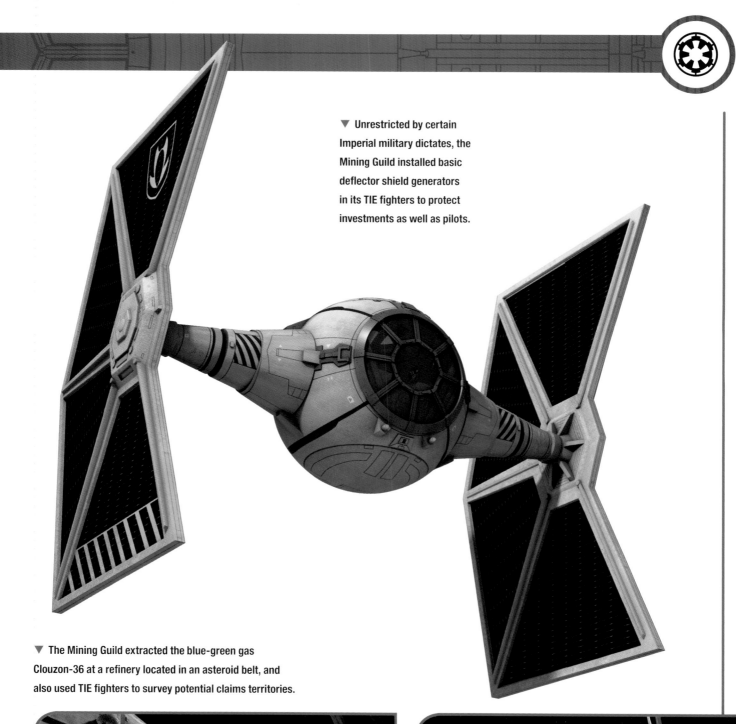

▼ Unrestricted by certain Imperial military dictates, the Mining Guild installed basic deflector shield generators in its TIE fighters to protect investments as well as pilots.

▼ The Mining Guild extracted the blue-green gas Clouzon-36 at a refinery located in an asteroid belt, and also used TIE fighters to survey potential claims territories.

SPECIFICATIONS TIE/mg MINING GUILD

MANUFACTURER: Sienar Fleet Systems

AFFILIATION: Mining Guild, Galactic Empire

MODEL: TIE/in starfighter

CLASS: Starfighter

LENGTH: 6.3 m (20 ft 10 in)

WIDTH: 6.9 m (22 ft 9 in)

HEIGHT: 8.8 m (28 ft 11 in)

MAXIMUM ACCELERATION: 4,000 G

MEGALIGHT PER HOUR: 95

MAXIMUM SPEED (ATMOSPHERE): 950 kph (590 mph)

ENGINE: SFS P-s4 twin ion engines

HYPERDRIVE: None

SHIELDING: Equipped

NAVIGATION SYSTEM: N-s6 Navcon

TARGETING SYSTEMS: T-s8 targeting computer

ARMAMENT: L-s1 laser cannons (2)

ESCAPE CRAFT: Ejector seat

CREW: Pilot (1)

LIFE SUPPORT: Equipped

CONSUMABLES: 1 day

COST: 40,000 credits

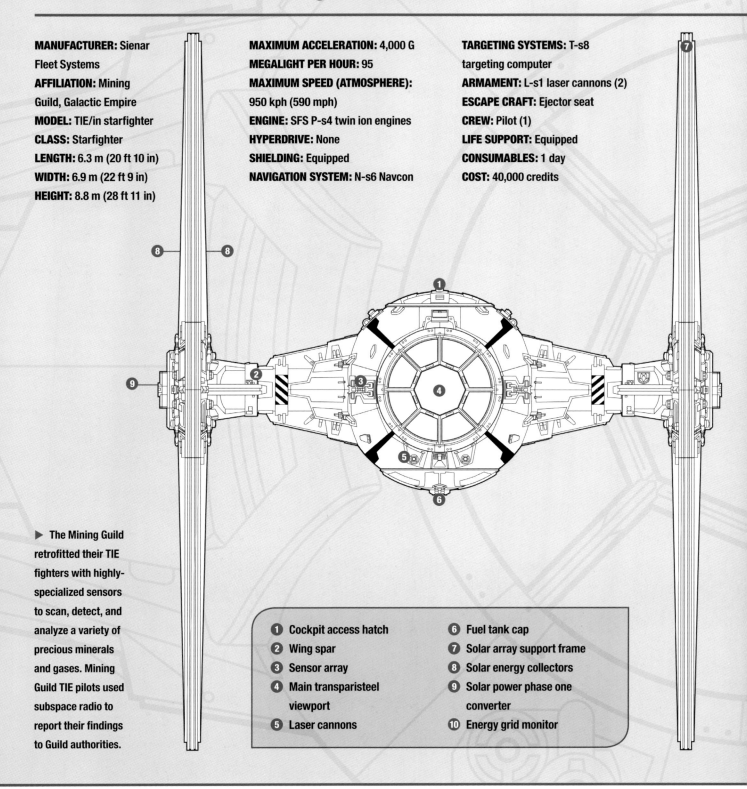

▶ The Mining Guild retrofitted their TIE fighters with highly-specialized sensors to scan, detect, and analyze a variety of precious minerals and gases. Mining Guild TIE pilots used subspace radio to report their findings to Guild authorities.

1. Cockpit access hatch
2. Wing spar
3. Sensor array
4. Main transparisteel viewport
5. Laser cannons
6. Fuel tank cap
7. Solar array support frame
8. Solar energy collectors
9. Solar power phase one converter
10. Energy grid monitor

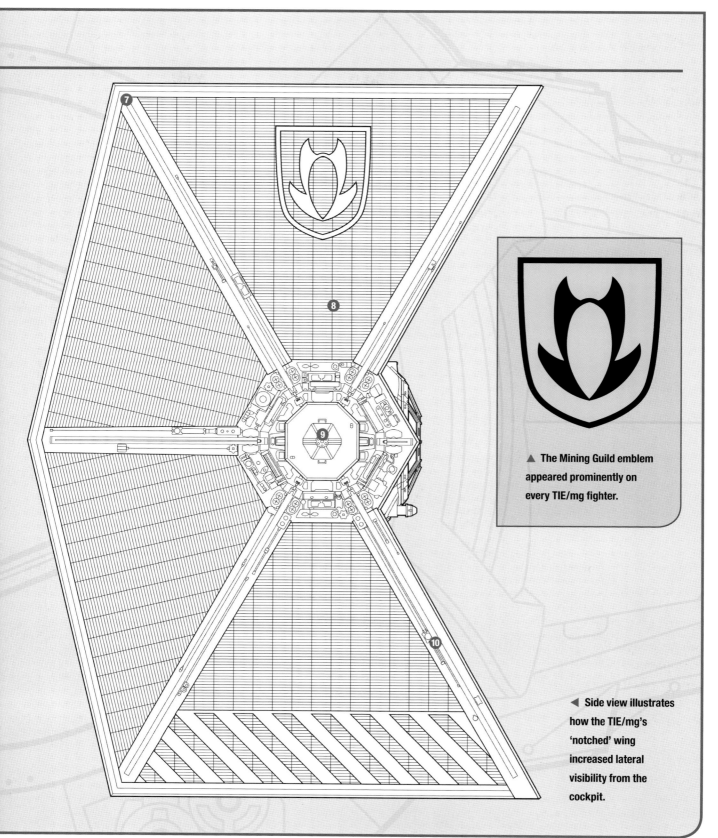

▲ The Mining Guild emblem appeared prominently on every TIE/mg fighter.

◀ Side view illustrates how the TIE/mg's 'notched' wing increased lateral visibility from the cockpit.

TIE/in INTERCEPTOR

Sixteen years after Supreme Chancellor Palpatine reshaped the Republic into the Empire, Imperial authorities realized they needed faster starfighters to combat the Rebel Alliance's growing fleet. However, after Sienar Fleet Systems calculated that a full production run of the TIE Advanced x1 would be prohibitively expensive, the Imperials knew they'd need another option. Imperial commanders and pilots met with Sienar officials and designers, and directed Sienar to develop a new starfighter that could surpass the Rebellion's X-wings and Y-wings.

The result was the TIE/in Interceptor, which was not only faster than most Rebel starfighters, but faster, more maneuverable, and more lethal than the standard TIE fighter. For economic and practical purposes, Sienar retained the standard TIE fighter's cockpit, but incorporated design innovations from the TIE Advanced x1. The innovations included twin SFS P-s5.6 ion engines for increased speed, inward-swept wings with broad solar panels to provide the necessary additional power input for the engines, and improved combat software. But unlike the TIE Advanced x1, the Interceptor's wings were dagger-shaped instead of

quadrangular, and had open "cutaway" areas between the upper and lower wings that gave the pilot improved lateral vision. Each of the four wingtips carried a mounted laser cannon, and the cockpit had mounts for two optional laser cannons. Sienar upgraded the Interceptor's fire-control computer's targeting software to allow faster response and more accurate tracking ability. Like the TIE/in fighter, the TIE Interceptor lacked defensive shields and a hyperdrive, but the Interceptor's armaments and maneuverability convinced many Imperial pilots that the Interceptor was not only a superior fighter, but that shields and hyperdrives were superfluous.

Sienar also developed a new system of ion stream projection for the Interceptor. The system featured finely-tuned twin-port deflectors that served to balance each other, allowing the pilot to execute tighter turns, prolonged rolls, and jinking maneuvers, while the Interceptor's bent wings compensated for any loss in stabilization. Updated ship maintenance monitoring software manipulated and controlled the twin-port deflectors automatically, allowing the pilot to better concentrate on targets.

◀ **By the time of the Battle of Endor, the TIE Interceptor and upgraded TIE/in models accounted for 20 percent of the Imperial Navy's starfighter fleet.**

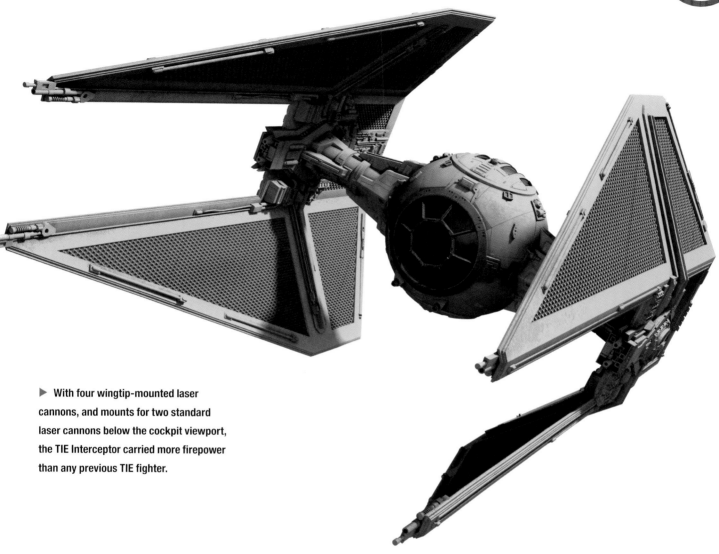

► With four wingtip-mounted laser cannons, and mounts for two standard laser cannons below the cockpit viewport, the TIE Interceptor carried more firepower than any previous TIE fighter.

► After the Battle of Endor, decommissioned Imperial starfighters, including TIE Interceptors, became available on the black market.

SPECIFICATIONS TIE/in INTERCEPTOR

MANUFACTURER: Sienar Fleet Systems

AFFILIATION: Galactic Empire

MODEL: TIE/in Interceptor

CLASS: Starfighter

LENGTH: 7.7 m (25 ft 3 in)

WIDTH: 6.5 m
(21 ft 5 in)

HEIGHT: 5.3 m
(17 ft 3 in)

MAXIMUM ACCELERATION: 4,240 G

MEGALIGHT PER HOUR: 110

MAXIMUM SPEED (ATMOSPHERE):
1,250 kph (777 mph)

ENGINE: SFS P-s5.6 twin ion engines
with ion stream projector

HYPERDRIVE: None

SHIELDING: None

NAVIGATION SYSTEM: N-s6 Navcon

TARGETING SYSTEMS: SFS T-s9a
targeting computer

ARMAMENT: Wingtip L-s9.3
laser cannons (4); chin-mounted
L-s9.3 laser cannons (2)

ESCAPE CRAFT: Ejector seat

CREW: Pilot (1)

❶ Cockpit access hatch	❹ Main transparisteel viewport	❼ Solar array support frame	❿ Energy grid monitor
❷ Wing spar	❺ Laser cannons	❽ Solar energy collectors	⓫ Advanced targeting
❸ Sensor array	❻ Fuel tank cap	❾ Solar power phase one converter	sensors

LIFE SUPPORT: Equipped

CONSUMABLES: 2 days

COST: 120,000 Imperial credits new; 50,000 used (military requisition charges)

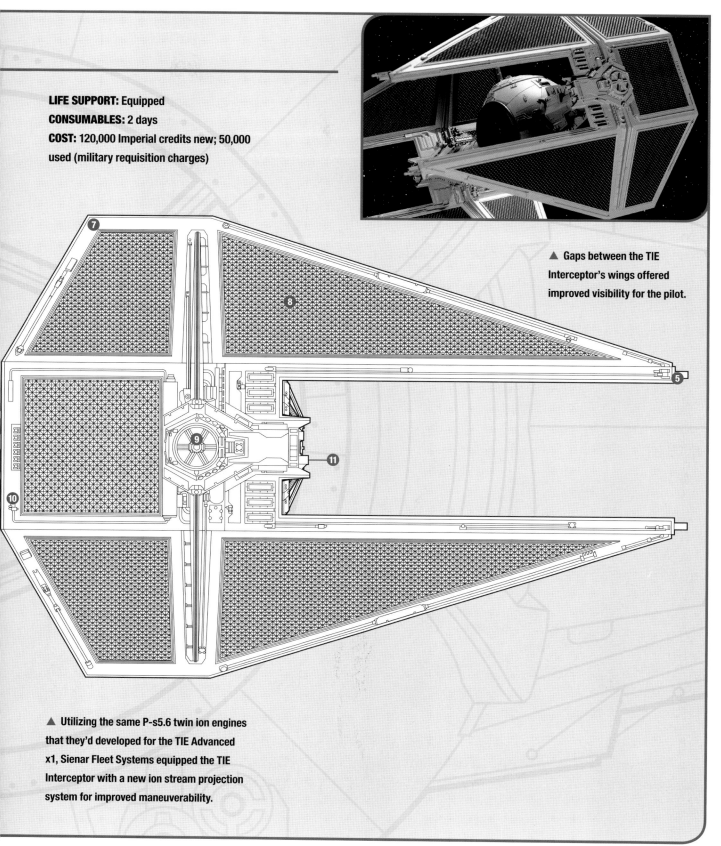

▲ Gaps between the TIE Interceptor's wings offered improved visibility for the pilot.

▲ Utilizing the same P-s5.6 twin ion engines that they'd developed for the TIE Advanced x1, Sienar Fleet Systems equipped the TIE Interceptor with a new ion stream projection system for improved maneuverability.

TIE/d DEFENDER

Two years before the Empire completed construction of the first Death Star battle station, Grand Admiral Thrawn, commander of the Imperial Seventh Fleet, spearheaded an initiative to develop a new Imperial starfighter. Thrawn's incentive for the initiative evolved after he examined briefings from Imperial Security Bureau agents who captured and interrogated renegade TIE fighter pilots who had attempted to defect to the Rebellion. From the briefings, Thrawn noted that all the pilots had expressed reluctance to operating starfighters that lacked energy shields and hyperdrives. Thrawn submitted a report to Grand Moff Tarkin, and persuaded Tarkin to consider how a new starfighter with a hyperdrive and improved offensive and defensive systems would be not only advantageous against Rebel fighters, but would also increase loyalty among

Imperial pilots. Although Tarkin asserted that standard unshielded TIE fighters were a more economical method to maintain authority over TIE pilots, he authorized Thrawn to proceed with his initiative, and to meet with designers at the Sienar Advanced Projects Laboratory on Lothal.

Thrawn was a remarkably proactive collaborator with Sienar, as he submitted specific design aspects for the new fighter, including that it would have three wings—similar to the "cutaway" dagger wings on the TIE Interceptor—mounted to an extended aft section behind the spherical cockpit module. Various accounts attested that Thrawn showed the designers a rare Kamino saberdart to convey the positions of the wings, and also how the design would give the pilot unparalleled visibility, and augment speed and maneuverability. Computer simulations verified that the

◀ **Faster than any previously manufactured TIE model, the TIE Defender was also equipped with a hyperdrive.**

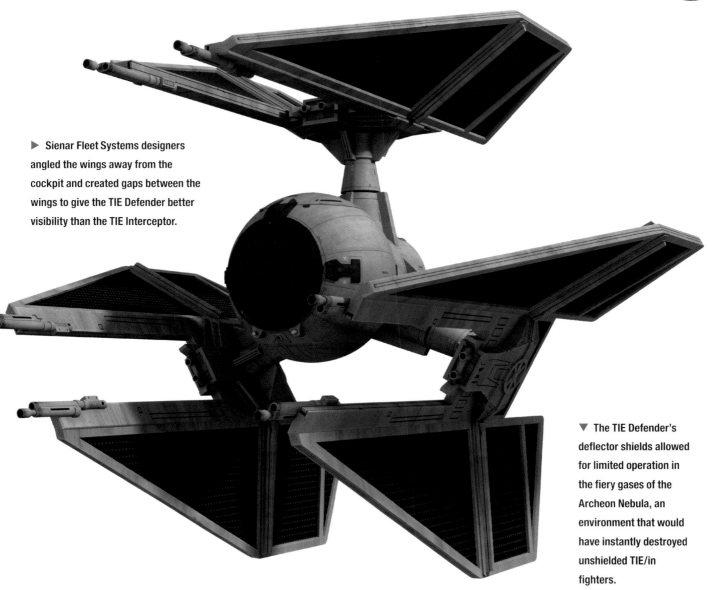

▶ Sienar Fleet Systems designers angled the wings away from the cockpit and created gaps between the wings to give the TIE Defender better visibility than the TIE Interceptor.

▼ The TIE Defender's deflector shields allowed for limited operation in the fiery gases of the Archeon Nebula, an environment that would have instantly destroyed unshielded TIE/in fighters.

design would be faster than Rebel Y-wing starfighters.

Sienar Fleet Systems created an experimental prototype, which they named the TIE/d Defender, and generally referred to as the TIE Defender. The TIE Defender's three solar-collector wings allowed for increased energy use, and were equipped with computer-controlled maneuvering jets. Each wing carried two laser cannons, while the bottom of the cockpit module held two warhead launchers. The TIE Defender's combined weaponry classified the vessel as a fighter-bomber.

Although the TIE Defender exceeded expectations, a series of setbacks and budgetary concerns discouraged the Empire from a large production run.

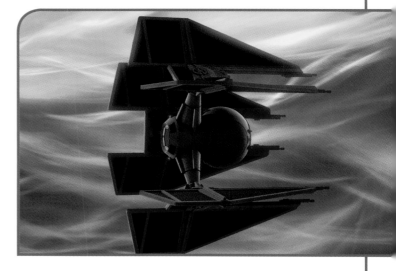

SPECIFICATIONS TIE/d DEFENDER

MANUFACTURER: Sienar Fleet Systems

AFFILIATION: Galactic Empire

MODEL: TIE/d Defender

CLASS: Starfighter

LENGTH: 8.8 m (28 ft 10 in)

WIDTH: 10 m (32 ft 11 in)

HEIGHT: 8.7 m (28 ft 7 in)

MAXIMUM ACCELERATION: 4,280 G

MEGALIGHT PER HOUR: 115

MAXIMUM SPEED (ATMOSPHERE): 1,680 kph (1,045 mph)

ENGINE: SFS P-sz9.7 twin ion engines

HYPERDRIVE: Class 2

SHIELDING: Equipped

NAVIGATION SYSTEM: SFS N-s6 Navcon

TARGETING SYSTEMS: T-s9a targeting computer

ARMAMENT: Wingtip L-s9.3 laser cannons (6); chin-mounted L-s9.3 laser cannons (2); warhead launchers; tractor beam projector

ESCAPE CRAFT: Ejector seat

CREW: Pilot (1)

LIFE SUPPORT: None

CONSUMABLES: 1 week

COST: 300,000 Imperial credits new; 80,000 used (military requisition charges)

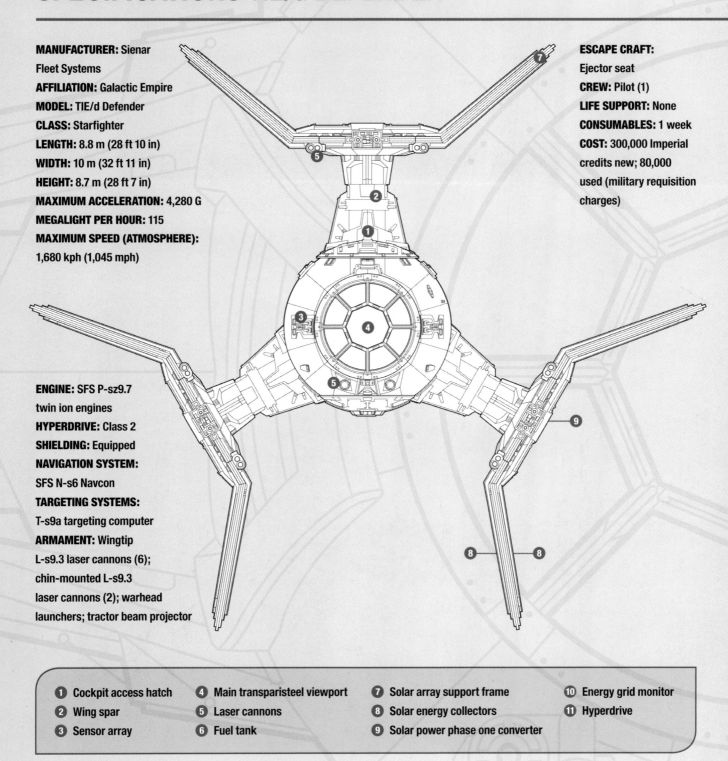

1. Cockpit access hatch
2. Wing spar
3. Sensor array
4. Main transparisteel viewport
5. Laser cannons
6. Fuel tank
7. Solar array support frame
8. Solar energy collectors
9. Solar power phase one converter
10. Energy grid monitor
11. Hyperdrive

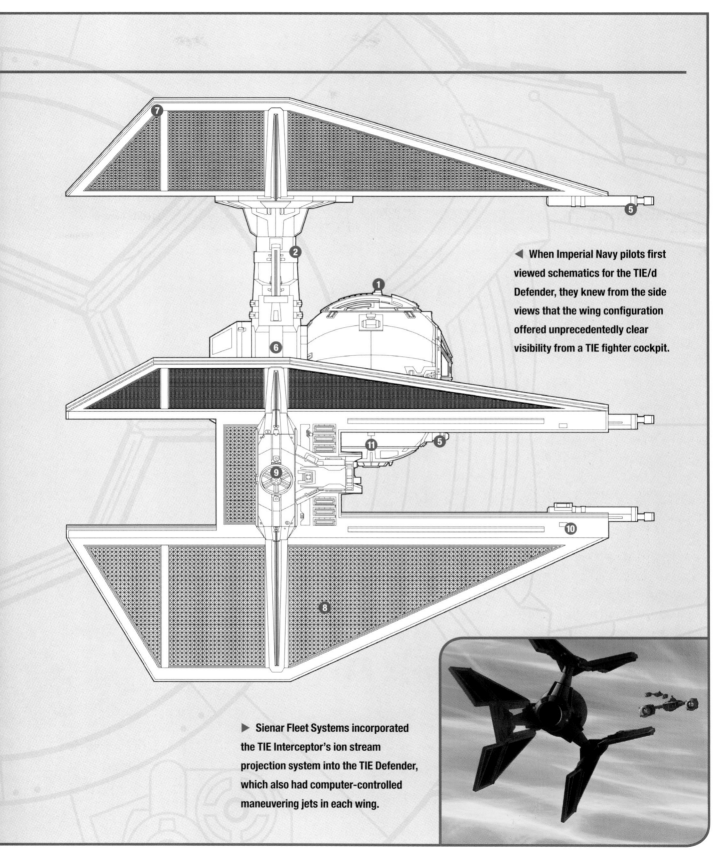

◀ When Imperial Navy pilots first
viewed schematics for the TIE/d
Defender, they knew from the side
views that the wing configuration
offered unprecedentedly clear
visibility from a TIE fighter cockpit.

▶ Sienar Fleet Systems incorporated
the TIE Interceptor's ion stream
projection system into the TIE Defender,
which also had computer-controlled
maneuvering jets in each wing.

TIE/d DEFENDER ELITE

After Grand Admiral Thrawn introduced the TIE/d Defender as part of his new starfighter initiative at the Imperial Factory on Lothal, Emperor Palpatine's lieutenant Darth Vader informed Thrawn that he believed the TIE Defender was an excellent ship, and that he had notified the Emperor of his support for Thrawn's project. Vader further recommended that the new Defender should have greater speed, more powerful armaments, and less complicated controls for pilots. Thrawn promptly relayed Vader's instructions to the Sienar Advanced Projects Laboratory's designers on Lothal.

Sienar dubbed the new prototype the TIE/d Defender Elite. Like the standard Defender, the Defender Elite had three dagger-tipped wings, eight heavy laser cannons, and a hyperdrive. Following a battery of tests in flight simulators, numerous sources from Sienar as well as Imperial pilots professed the craft's speed and maneuverability outperformed nearly every other starfighter produced at the time.

Unfortunately, on the day that Thrawn and Imperial Governor Arihnda Pryce readied to watch Imperial Navy Commander Vult Skerris pilot the Defender Elite prototype

for its first actual test flight, Rebel Alliance insurgents stole the prototype. Thrawn had reason to believe one of the rebels was Ezra Bridger, a Lothal youth with limited experience as a pilot. Deciding to exploit the situation as an improvised flight test, Thrawn dispatched three Imperial pilots in TIE Interceptors to pursue the Defender Elite. After Bridger

▲ Virtually identical to the TIE/d Defender, the Defender Elite was faster and equipped with more weapons.

◀ The Imperial Navy tested the TIE Defender Elite on the planet Lothal.

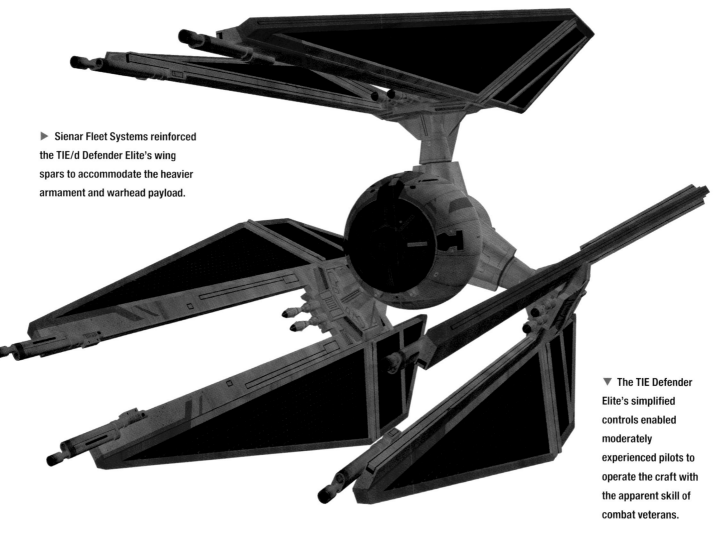

▶ Sienar Fleet Systems reinforced the TIE/d Defender Elite's wing spars to accommodate the heavier armament and warhead payload.

▼ The TIE Defender Elite's simplified controls enabled moderately experienced pilots to operate the craft with the apparent skill of combat veterans.

managed to shoot down all three Interceptors, Thrawn concluded that the Defender Elite could transform even a novice pilot into a deadly ace. He also authorized Governor Price to activate a kill switch, a security precaution that triggered an explosion on the Defender Elite and caused the fighter to crash. But by the time Imperial authorities arrived at the crash site, the rebels had already escaped with the Elite's hyperdrive and flight recorder.

Just as Thrawn was determined to begin mass production of the TIE Defender Elite at the Imperial Armory Complex on Lothal, the Rebel Alliance was determined to stop him. The Alliance Fleet attacked, and in the battle that ensued, the Empire lost most of the TIE Defender Elite factories and also a crucial fuel depot. The losses prompted Imperial officials to halt the TIE Defender project indefinitely, and shift their attention to finishing construction of the Death Star.

HYPERDRIVE

For the TIE/d Defender, Grand Admiral Thrawn commissioned Sienar Fleet Systems to equip the starfighter with a hyperdrive. Because Sienar had already created a Class 4 hyperdrive for the TIE Advanced x1 prototype, Sienar proposed to incorporate the same unit into the Defender. However, Thrawn insisted that the Defender should have a Class 2 hyperdrive, which would allow the starfighter to keep pace across hyperspace with Imperial Star Destroyers. Sienar complied.

Sienar designed the Defender with a ventral socket to house the hyperdrive, a cylindrical drum-shaped Class 2 unit that was remarkably compact and lightweight. Subsequently, Sienar used the same hyperdrive for the TIE/d Defender Elite. Unfortunately, budgetary reasons prompted the Imperial Navy to end production of the TIE Defender and divert all funding to the Death Star battle station.

TOP

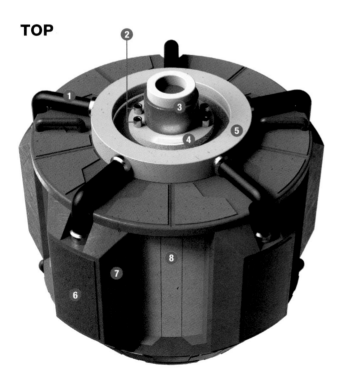

BOTTOM

1. Power conduits
2. Booster power lines
3. High current power base
4. Optical data interface
5. Energizer ring
6. Processor cooling plates
7. Secondary processor housings
8. Main reaction chamber
9. Maintenance access panels
10. Effect channels
11. Energy stabilizers
12. Null field stabilizer

SPECIFICATIONS TIE/d DEFENDER ELITE

MANUFACTURER: Sienar Advanced Projects Laboratory
AFFILIATION: Galactic Empire
MODEL: TIE/d Defender Elite
CLASS: Starfighter
LENGTH: 11.3 m (37 ft 1 in)
WIDTH: 10 m (32 ft 11 in)
HEIGHT: 8.7 m (28 ft 7 in)

MAXIMUM ACCELERATION: 4,300 G
MEGALIGHT PER HOUR: 120
MAXIMUM SPEED (ATMOSPHERE): 1,800 kph (1,118 mph)
ENGINE: SFS P-sz9.7 twin ion engines
HYPERDRIVE: Class 2
SHIELDING: Equipped
NAVIGATION SYSTEM: SFS N-s6.1 Navcon

TARGETING SYSTEMS: Glucon CRX-9 targeting computer
ARMAMENT: Wingtip L-s9.3 laser cannons (6); chin-mounted L-s9.3 laser cannons (2); warhead launchers; tractor beam projector
ESCAPE CRAFT: Ejector seat
CREW: Pilot (1)
LIFE SUPPORT: None
CONSUMABLES: 5 days
COST: 310,000 Imperial credits new; 90,000 used (military requisition charges)

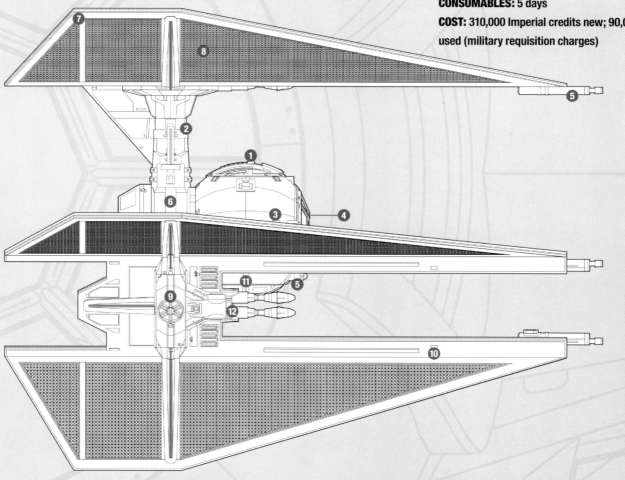

❶ Cockpit access hatch	❹ Main transparisteel viewport	❼ Solar array support frame	❿ Energy grid monitor
❷ Wing spar	❺ Laser cannons	❽ Solar energy collectors	⓫ Hyperdrive
❸ Sensor array	❻ Fuel tank	❾ Solar power phase one converter	⓬ Warhead launchers

TIE/sk x1 (AKA TIE STRIKER)

After the fall of the Republic, Governor Wilhuff Tarkin founded the Tarkin Initiative, a secret think tank within the Advanced Weapons Research division of the Imperial Security Bureau. Headquartered in the heart of the Citadel, an Imperial military industrial complex on the remote, tropical world Scarif, the Tarkin Initiative developed and tested next-generation designs for Imperial war machines. One such design was the TIE/sk x1 experimental air superiority fighter, or TIE striker.

The Tarkin Initiative conceived the streamlined variant of the standard TIE/in specifically for atmospheric patrols over Imperial ground-based installations because they were aware of the TIE/in's disadvantages in atmospheric maneuvers. The TIE/in's lightweight construction and large hexagonal solar arrays were vulnerable to crosswinds and difficult to steer outside of a vacuum, and also vulnerable to enemy pilots who knew how to exploit the TIE/in's limitations. To augment aerodynamic efficiency and durability, Sienar Fleet Systems outfitted the TIE striker with a larger command pod that served as a greater central, stabilizing mass, and two tilting, servo-mounted wings that pilots could angle downward to add extra protection to the

▲ With a maximum speed of 1,500 kph, TIE strikers could travel 450 kph faster than enemy X-wing starfighters in atmospheres.

pod. The enlarged, pressurized cockpit accommodated a pilot and an optional bombardier/gunner.

Like the TIE/in, the TIE striker had twin ion engines that supplied forward thrust, but had a more aerodynamic

◄ Sienar Fleet Systems armed the TIE striker with L-s9.3 laser cannons, the same primary weapons of the TIE Advanced x1 and the TIE/in interceptor.

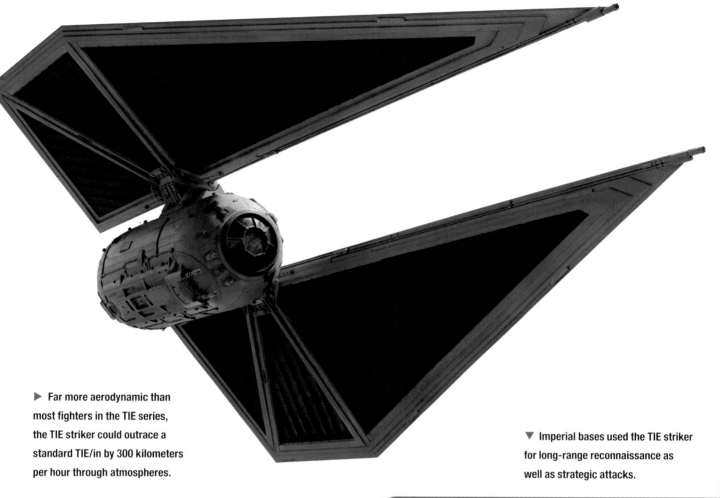

▶ Far more aerodynamic than most fighters in the TIE series, the TIE striker could outrace a standard TIE/in by 300 kilometers per hour through atmospheres.

▼ Imperial bases used the TIE striker for long-range reconnaissance as well as strategic attacks.

design, and also more advanced and specialized repulsorlifts for atmospheric operations. The repulsorlifts reduced the craft's overall weight, and gave the ion engines greater thrust. Although the TIE striker was capable of suborbital flight, designers and military commanders agreed the craft would be most effective when deployed in low to high atmospheric defense scenarios. Because SFS built the TIE striker strictly for planetary missions, the craft had no need for a hyperdrive.

The TIE striker's inventors were confident that Imperial commanders would welcome the atmospheric fighter as a practical alternative to TIE/in fighters for planetary combat missions. Although TIE pilots appreciated the advantages of the TIE striker, Imperial admiralty regarded the craft as a wasteful expenditure, and maintained that standard TIE fighters and TIE bombers were sufficient for planetary theaters of war. Consequently, SFS manufactured the TIE striker in relatively limited production runs.

SPECIFICATIONS TIE/sk x1 (AKA TIE STRIKER)

MANUFACTURER: Sienar Fleet Systems

AFFILIATION: Galactic Empire

MODEL: TIE/sk x1 experimental air superiority fighter

CLASS: Starfighter

LENGTH: 17.2 m (56 ft 4 in)

WIDTH: 11.3 m (37 ft 1 in)

HEIGHT: 3 m (9 ft 8 in)

MAXIMUM ACCELERATION: Not applicable to aircraft

MEGALIGHT PER HOUR: Not applicable to aircraft

MAXIMUM SPEED (ATMOSPHERE): 1,500 kph (932 mph)

ENGINE: Twin ion engines; repulsorlifts

HYPERDRIVE: None

SHIELDING: None

NAVIGATION SYSTEM: SFS N-a1 Navcon

TARGETING SYSTEMS: T-a9a targeting computer

ARMAMENT: Fire-linked SFS L-s9.3 laser cannons (4); H-s1 heavy laser cannons (2); proton bomb chute (1)

ESCAPE CRAFT: Ejector seats

CREW: Pilot (1); optional bombardier/gunner (1)

LIFE SUPPORT: Equipped

CONSUMABLES: 1 day

COST: 70,000 Imperial credits new; 30,000 used (military requisition charges)

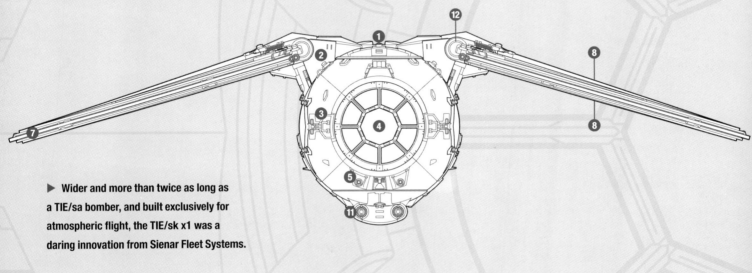

▶ Wider and more than twice as long as a TIE/sa bomber, and built exclusively for atmospheric flight, the TIE/sk x1 was a daring innovation from Sienar Fleet Systems.

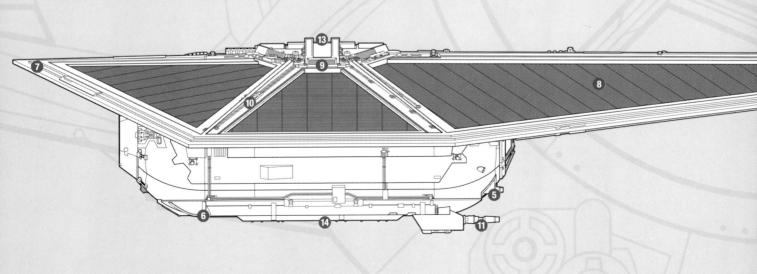

▲ Carrying four laser cannons, two heavy laser cannons, and a proton bomb chute, the TIE striker was one of the most weaponized TIE fighters in the Imperial fleet.

▲ For the TIE/sk x1's tapered wings, Sienar Fleet Systems utilized micro-corrugated solar panels similar to the panels on the TIE/rb heavy starfighter.

1 Cockpit access hatch
2 Foil articulation motor housing
3 Sensor array
4 Main transparisteel viewport
5 Laser cannons
6 Fuel tank cap
7 Solar array support frame
8 Solar energy collectors
9 Solar power phase one converter
10 Energy grid monitor
11 Heavy laser cannons
12 Articulated joint
13 Magnatomic locking mechanism
14 Ventral bomb port

TIE/rp REAPER ATTACK LANDER

To transfer Imperial troops and vehicles from orbital warships and space stations to and from planetary surfaces, the Imperial Navy typically utilized dropship transports or shuttles, such as the Sienar Fleet Systems-manufactured Sentinel-class shuttle. But after Imperial Intelligence began training stormtroopers to become special-mission commando death troopers, Grand Moff Tarkin authorized Intelligence to conscript Sienar to design and engineer a high-performance twin ion engine transport to deliver elite Imperial troops into battle zones. The result was the TIE/rp Reaper attack lander, or TIE reaper.

Sienar modeled the TIE reaper prototype after the relatively smaller TIE striker, which Sienar also designed for maneuvering primarily through atmospheres. Like the TIE striker, the TIE reaper had two long, dagger-shaped solar energy-collecting wings, advanced ailerons that enabled precise atmospheric maneuvering. But because the TIE reaper was nearly twice the length of the TIE striker, and had a substantially larger fuselage rather than a compact cockpit module, a broad, horizontal stabilizer was hinged between the aft sections of the articulated wings.

Unlike most Imperial TIE-series ships, the TIE reaper had energy shield projectors in addition to thick armor plating. Although the Imperial Navy regarded the TIE reaper's death trooper passengers as expendable as the average storm trooper, Imperial Intelligence maintained that that energy shields were a small but justified investment to make the most of the Empire's investment for the death troopers' training. As further protection, the TIE reaper usually traveled with an escort of at least three TIE strikers. The TIE reaper also carried two powerful laser cannons, and was equipped with sensor-jamming technology, used to jam or disrupt sensors on enemy vessels.

The TIE reaper boasted a powerful repulsorlift engine that enabled the craft to come to a swift, hovering stop less than a meter above a planet's surface. A ventral hatch-ramp allowed the death troopers to deploy immediately, without any need to wait for the ship to touch down. The repulsorlifts also enabled the TIE reaper to launch and ascend at remarkable speed for a ship of its size.

◀ Although built primarily for atmospheric flights, the hyperdrive-equipped TIE striker was fully operational in space. TIE strikers typically served as escorts for the TIE reaper, and defended the TIE reaper's passengers against enemy fire.

and one ventral heavy laser cannon turret. In addition to spacious cargo holds, the freighter had large brigs that contained multiple cell blocks for enemies of the Empire. Such freighters routinely transported captives to prisons and labor camps, such as the spice mines of Kessel and the Spire on Stygeon Prime.

The freighter also carried a complement of up to four TIE fighters that protected the vessel against enemy ships. Because standard TIE fighters lacked hyperdrive engines, the Empire also relied on *Gozanti*-class cruisers to swiftly deliver TIE fighters to remote battle zones. Extendible docking tubes, located below the cruiser's port and starboard wings, clamped onto fighters and allowed pilots direct access from the freighter to their respective TIE fighter cockpits. TIE pilots typically traveled aboard the freighter during missions through hyperspace, and flew their fighters as escorts when the freighter traveled along routes frequented by pirates and rebels.

The Imperial *Gozanti*-class cruiser had a variant, the *Gozanti*-class Assault Carrier. The variant could also transport up to four TIE fighters, but a reinforced hull and more powerful repulsorlift engines enabled the vessel's ventral magnetic docking claws to carry an alternate cargo of two two Imperial AT-DP or AT-AT walkers.

▲ The Empire also utilized the *Gozanti*-class cruiser to transport AT-DP walkers to and from planetary surfaces.

▼ Because TIE/in fighters lacked hyperdrives, the Imperial Navy relied on *Gozanti*-class cruisers and other vessels to deliver starfighters across the galaxy.

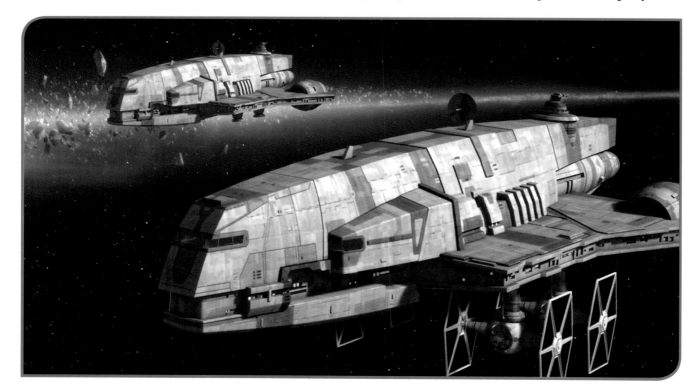

TIE FIGHTER

FIRST ORDER TIE FIGHTERS

"Pilots of the First Order. We assemble here today in remembrance of our forebears, and in recognition of those who laid the foundation for our own military organization.

Fifty-two years ago today, Supreme Chancellor Palpatine declared his intention to reorganize the Republic into the first Galactic Empire. He assured his citizens that the Empire would provide a safe and secure society, a society that would last for ten thousand years. But as any historian in the New Republic will be quick to inform you, the Emperor's plans fell—or rather seemed to fall—considerably short of his goals.

You all know what happened. The Rebel Alliance, using single-pilot starfighters, destroyed the Empire's first Death Star at the Battle of Yavin. Four years later, the rebels destroyed the second Death Star at Endor. And a year after that, Imperials surrendered at Jakku, and signed the Galactic Concordance, effectively ending their war with the rebels. The Imperials also ended all recruitment activity, abandoned their military academies and outposts, and relinquished their claim to Coruscant.

And yet now, 28 years after Imperials signed the Concordance, here we are.

Under the command of the Supreme Leader, we have secured this planet as a base, and transformed it into our stronghold and our most powerful weapon. Our contemporary military academies offer more advanced training for officers, pilots, soldiers, and technicians than any other so-called civilization in the galaxy. And while the peacemongering senators of the New Republic do their useless best to enfeeble their government, our numbers grow stronger every day. Even more so, we grow stronger every day.

And I dare say we are not only stronger than our forebears, but wiser too. Because just as we have adopted certain Imperial ideals, we have also learned from Imperial errors. Perhaps their greatest errors were underestimating their enemies, and undervaluing their own troops. As any of our tactical simulation computers will confirm, had the Imperial Navy outfitted their TIE fighters with even basic energy shielding systems, the outcomes of the two Death Star battles would have been very different.

Senior officers of the First Order know the value of loyal, dedicated, highly skilled pilots. We do not consider a single pilot expendable. Proper indoctrination and training takes time, and the First Order has invested heavily into every one of you. And because you'll be piloting shield-equipped TIE fighters, we are confident that our investment will pay off again and again and again.

There was a time when citizens of the galaxy obeyed rules of conduct and respected military power. They obeyed because they knew if they did not, Star Destroyers would arrive in orbit of their worlds. And those same Star Destroyers would unleash scores of TIE fighters, which would rain down upon every city and homestead, and reduce all to ruins.

For the Empire, that time is not past. But for the First Order, that time is just beginning."

— General Armitage Hux, First Order High Command, addressing troops at Starkiller Base on the 52nd anniversary of Empire Day.

TIE/fo SPACE SUPERIORITY FIGHTER

Like its Imperial predecessor, the First Order TIE fighter, or TIE/fo space superiority fighter, is a single-pilot attack craft with twin ion engines, a central spherical pod that houses the cockpit, and two hexagonal solar energy-collecting wings. And like the Imperial TIE, the TIE/fo lacks a hyperdrive, which limits the craft's uses to short-range missions and combat. However, the First Order utilized various technological advances to make the TIE/fo structurally stronger and more deadly than the standard Imperial TIE.

First Order designers equipped the TIE/fo with compact deflector shield generators that offer substantial protection against enemy fire, and which also provide a smoother passage through atmospheres and greater atmospheric control without requiring streamlined modifications to the spaceframe. The craft's power plant is a Sienar-Jaemus Fleet Systems I-a4b solar ionization reactor that has no moving parts to reduce maintenance. The TIE/fo's primary weapons are a pair of SJFS L-s9.6 laser cannons. Despite an obvious resemblance to the Imperial TIE, the TIE/fo boasts improved solar cells and higher-capacity energy converters. The TIE/fo's wings gather solar energy, and the energy travels through high-efficiency power lines to the craft's reactor, where the energy triggers emissions from a high-pressure radioactive fuel. The Sienar-Jaemus Fleet Systems I-a4b solar ionization reactor has no moving parts to reduce maintenance, and the engine thrusters are positioned to give the craft greater maneuverability than Imperial-era TIE fighters.

The shield generators in the TIE/fo not only protect the pilot but serve to illustrate a significant difference between the Empire and the First Order: the Empire—which had virtually unlimited resources for recruiting and training TIE fighter pilots—regarded Imperial pilots as essentially expendable, whereas the First Order values pilots as key military assets. Although the TIE/fo costs more to manufacture than the Imperial TIE fighter, First Order leaders believe their investment will pay off with more loyal and dedicated pilots, and eventual victory over the Resistance.

◀ The hulls of First Order TIE fighters are substantially darker than previous ships in the TIE series, making the TIE/in a more difficult target to spacefaring enemies who rely primarily on visual scanning and sensors.

▶ The First Order's standard TIE fighter is essentially an advanced version of the ubiquitous TIE/in that served the Imperial Navy during the Galactic Civil War.

◀ The TIE/fo fighter's rudimentary deflector shields smooth the passage through atmospheres, and give the fighters greater atmospheric control without requiring streamlined modifications to their space frames.

CUTAWAY

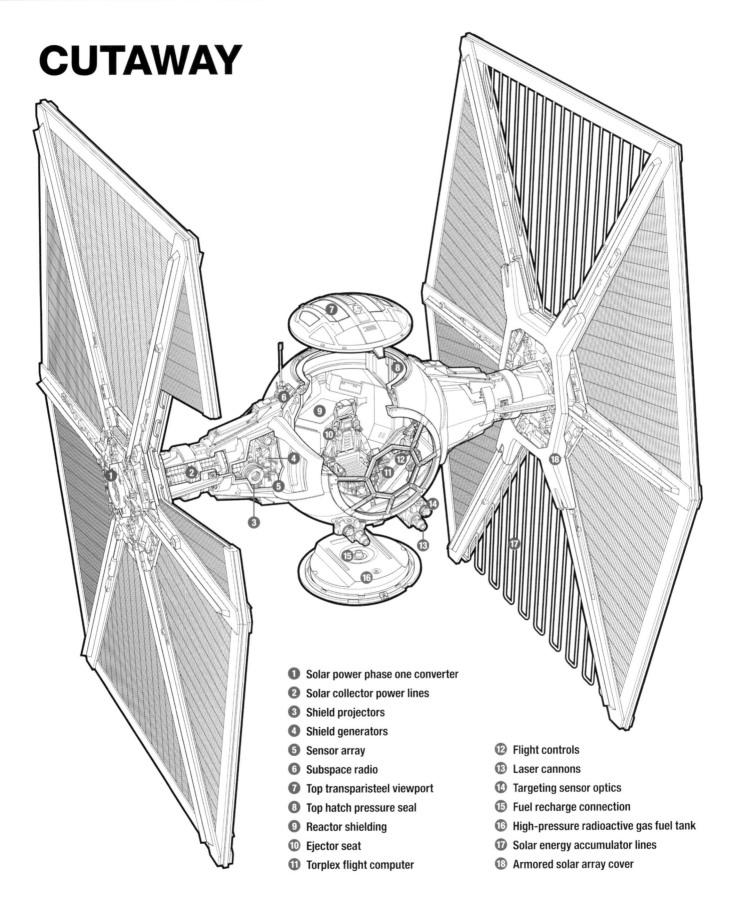

1. Solar power phase one converter
2. Solar collector power lines
3. Shield projectors
4. Shield generators
5. Sensor array
6. Subspace radio
7. Top transparisteel viewport
8. Top hatch pressure seal
9. Reactor shielding
10. Ejector seat
11. Torplex flight computer
12. Flight controls
13. Laser cannons
14. Targeting sensor optics
15. Fuel recharge connection
16. High-pressure radioactive gas fuel tank
17. Solar energy accumulator lines
18. Armored solar array cover

FRONT VIEW

Despite an obvious resemblance to the Imperial TIE/in fighter, the TIE/fo boasts many technological advancements, including high-efficiency energy coils, compact shield generators, an enhanced communications antenna, and deadlier firepower. While Imperial war ministries might have debated or discouraged the implementation of such innovations, First Order engineers thrive under a less bureaucratic regime.

AFT VIEW

Unlike the Imperial TIE/in fighter, which featured ion engines on either side of a solar ionization reactor, the TIE/fo fighter's SJFS P-s6 twin ion engines are positioned above and below the SJFS I-a4b reactor, a configuration that First Order engineers and pilots hail as a significant improvement for maneuverability.

SPECIFICATIONS TIE/fo SPACE SUPERIORITY FIGHTER

MANUFACTURER:
Sienar-Jaemus
Fleet Systems

AFFILIATION: First Order

MODEL: TIE/fo space
superiority fighter

CLASS: Starfighter

LENGTH: 6.7 m (22 ft)

WIDTH: 6.3 m (20 ft 10 in)

HEIGHT: 8.2 m (26 ft 10 in)

MAXIMUM ACCELERATION: 4,400 G

MEGALIGHT PER HOUR: 130

MAXIMUM SPEED (ATMOSPHERE):
1,200 kph (746 mph)

ENGINE: SJFS P-s6 twin ion engine

HYPERDRIVE: None

SHIELDING: Deflector shields

NAVIGATION SYSTEM:
Torplex flight computer

TARGETING SYSTEMS: T-sj1a
targeting computer

ARMAMENT: L-s9.6 laser cannons (2)

ESCAPE CRAFT: Ejector seat

CREW: Pilot (1)

LIFE SUPPORT: None

CONSUMABLES: 1 day

COST: 90,000 credits

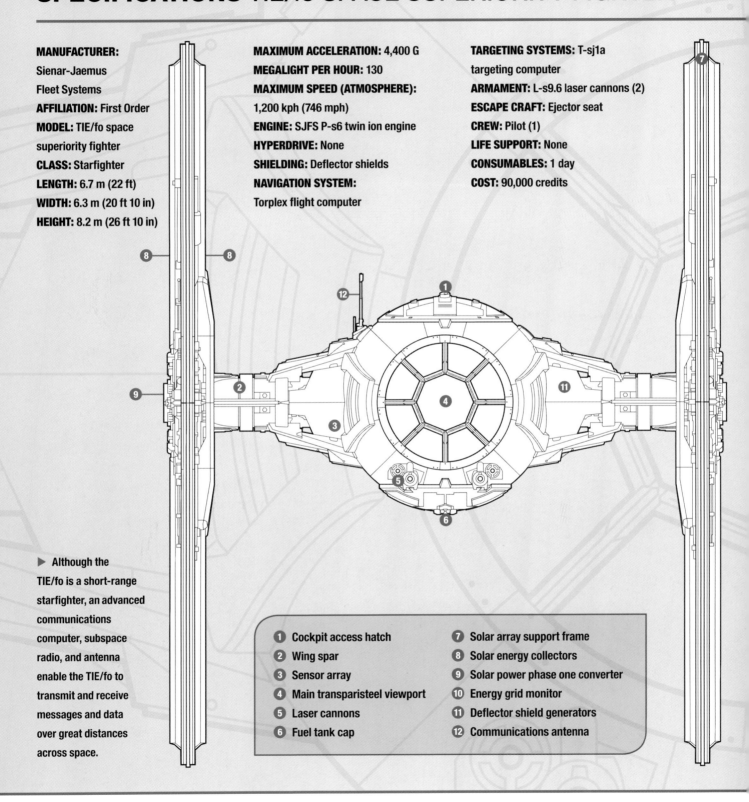

▶ Although the
TIE/fo is a short-range
starfighter, an advanced
communications
computer, subspace
radio, and antenna
enable the TIE/fo to
transmit and receive
messages and data
over great distances
across space.

1 Cockpit access hatch

2 Wing spar

3 Sensor array

4 Main transparisteel viewport

5 Laser cannons

6 Fuel tank cap

7 Solar array support frame

8 Solar energy collectors

9 Solar power phase one converter

10 Energy grid monitor

11 Deflector shield generators

12 Communications antenna

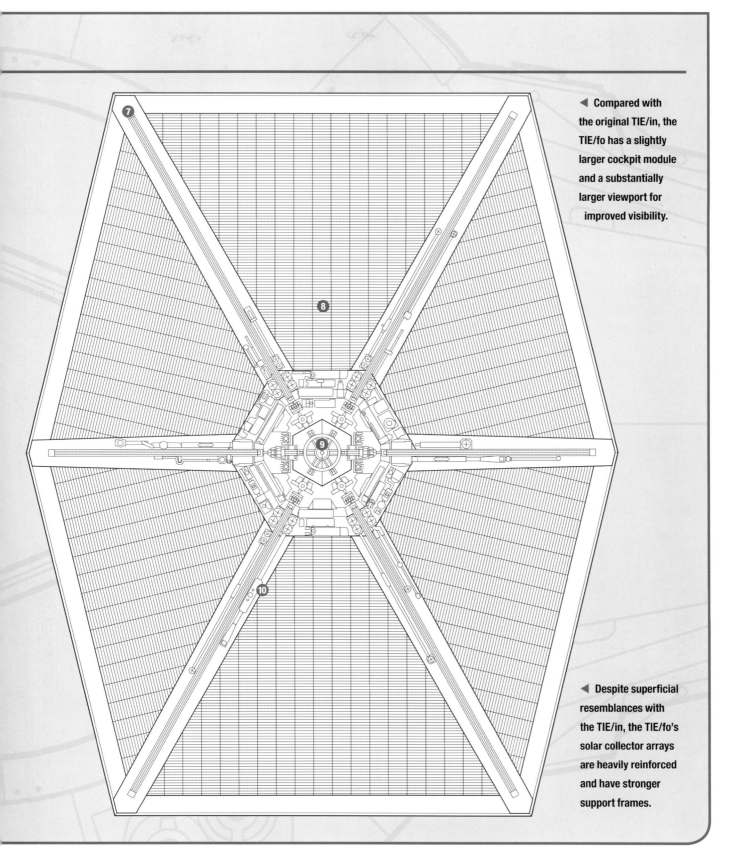

◀ Compared with the original TIE/in, the TIE/fo has a slightly larger cockpit module and a substantially larger viewport for improved visibility.

◀ Despite superficial resemblances with the TIE/in, the TIE/fo's solar collector arrays are heavily reinforced and have stronger support frames.

TIE/fo COCKPIT

After Imperial loyalists decamped to the Unknown Regions and founded the First Order, their representatives discreetly contacted their confidants at the starship manufacturer Sienar Fleet Systems. First Order officers knew they would need starfighters for their new fleet, and they wanted to secure a contract with Sienar to provide the First Order with TIE fighter simulator pods for training potential pilots, and also to construct a manufacturing facility for TIE fighters. Sienar administrators agreed with the provision that all transactions with the First Order would be kept in strict confidence from the New Republic, at least until the First Order officially revealed their fleet to the galaxy.

Sienar designers were surprised and also pleased to learn that the First Order leaders wanted to do more than merely recycle the Imperial TIE fighter. Unlike the Imperial Army and Navy, which had the authority and wherewithal to openly recruit and conscript civilians from across the galaxy, and also disposed of troops as if they were an unlimited resource, the First Order had limited numbers. The First Order was determined to make the most of every soldier and pilot that they had, and make each soldier and pilot aware of their own value to the First Order. To accomplish that goal, First Order officers and Sienar designers arrived at a decision that was in direct opposition to Imperial doctrine: the new TIE fighter would have deflector shields and a cockpit with built-in life-support systems.

Although the First Order TIE fighter's cockpit is in many ways similar to the Imperial version, the hull and structural reinforcements are much stronger, and the access hatch has a pressurized seal to contain the air that circulates inside the cockpit. Sienar designers made many subtle modifications to the fighter's interior to make the pilots more comfortable without making them less alert. Modifications include ergonomic data interfaces, adjustable temperature controls, and a form-fitting backpad on the ejector seat.

◀ Although the TIE/fo cockpit's life-support systems enable pilots to breathe freely without their helmets, pilots wear their sensor-laden helmets during combat missions to utilize enhanced targeting technologies.

▶ Sienar Fleet Systems began production of the TIE/fo cockpit and related components before the company reorganized as Sienar-Jaemus Fleet Systems.

TIE COCKPIT

1. Top hatch
2. Ejector seat
3. Seat restraints
4. Targeting computer column
5. Processor housing
6. Control handles
7. Throttle
8. Pivoting base
9. Reactor shielding
10. Hatch controls
11. Shield power management
12. Environmental controls
13. Power distribution controls
14. Sensor panel
15. Ejector seat arming lever
16. Ejector seat release

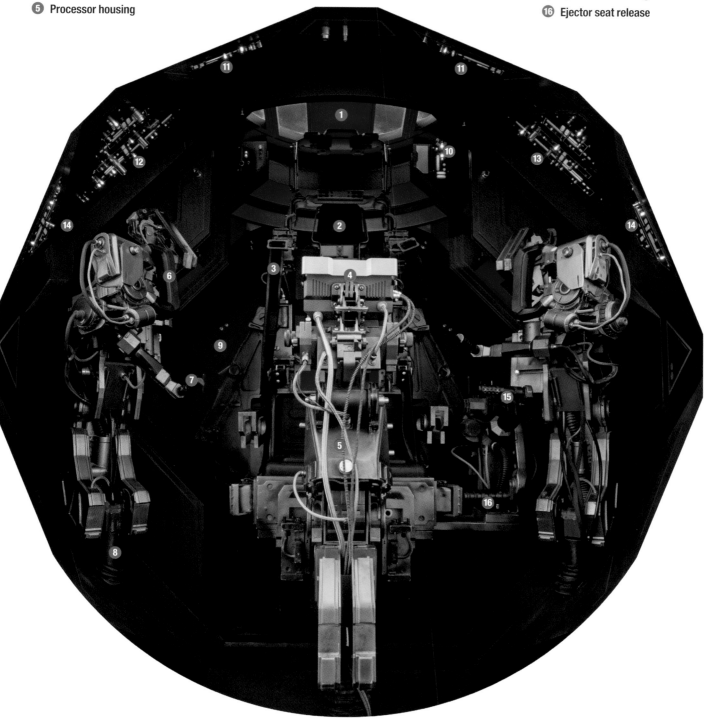

TIE/fo CONTROLS

The First Order TIE pilot's flight controls have adjustable control columns for each hand, a weapons trigger on the right-hand column, and a weapon interface that provides data displays for weapon operations. As the pilot shifts the control columns, a sophisticated Torplex flight computer translates the pilot's movements into micro-adjustments to operate and maneuver the twin ion streams that propel the fighter. After the initial production of the TIE/fo, the First Order commissioned Sienar-Jaemus Fleet Systems to design a First Order Special Forces TIE fighter, the TIE/sf, with a cockpit outfitted for a pilot and a rear-facing gunner. Instead of reinventing flight and weapons controls for the TIE/sf, SFJS engineers repurposed the TIE/fo controls for the TIE/sf, but relocated the pilot's central targeting computer display to the gunner's controls. TIE/sf pilots relied on either their helmets' built-in targeting interface projectors or their own keen eyes and reflexes to fire at targets.

▼ A side view of a First Order TIE fighter's left-hand control column exhibits the intricately engineered assembly of durable and adjustable military-grade SFJS components.

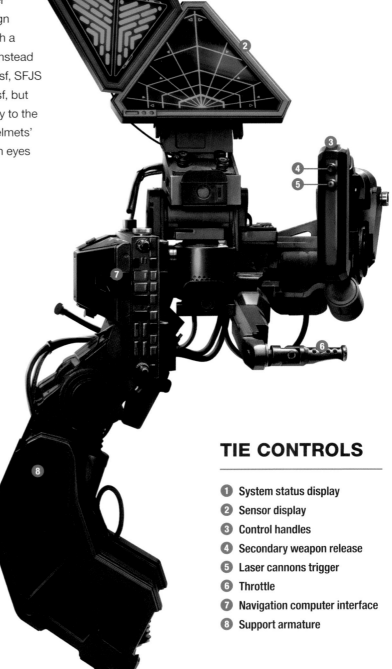

TIE CONTROLS

1. System status display
2. Sensor display
3. Control handles
4. Secondary weapon release
5. Laser cannons trigger
6. Throttle
7. Navigation computer interface
8. Support armature

◀ Sensor panels and controls for shield power management, environmental and life-support systems, and power distribution are set within the curved walls of each First Order TIE fighter cockpit.

9 Targeting computer
10 Weapon select
11 Target select
12 Processor housing
13 Combat systems display
14 Communications
15 Height adjust
16 Pivoting base

TIE/sf SPACE SUPERIORITY FIGHTER

An elite military unit, the First Order Special Forces take on the most challenging and hazardous missions to achieve the First Order's goals, and specialize in long-range reconnaissance and demolition operations. To accomplish such missions, the unit flies a Special Forces TIE fighter, a two-seat TIE/sf, which Sienar-Jaemus Fleet Systems equipped with a Class 2 miniaturized hyperdrive, and a more powerful weapons package than the standard First Order TIE fighter. TIE/sf pilots wear flight suits equipped with life-support systems, but because missions may require hours of travel through hyperspace, the TIE/sf's pressurized cockpit allows pilots to remove their helmets while operating the craft.

The TIE/sf's primary weapons are its front-facing SJFS L-s9.6 laser cannons; the secondary weapons are an SJFS Lb-14 dual heavy laser turret and a Kuat Drive Yards Arakyd missile launcher that fires ST7 concussion missiles and mag-pulse warheads. The laser turret rotates 360 degrees but at limited angles, as safety systems prevent the cannons from firing at the craft's own wings. A lone pilot can operate the TIE/sf and all its weapons from the cockpit's

forward-facing seat, but the TIE/sf is most effective with a gunner in the rear-facing seat, controlling the laser turret and missile launcher. The gunner uses a left-hand toggle to switch between laser cannon, missiles, and mag-pulse, and uses triggers on the right-hand grip to fire weapons. A targeting display presents data for the gunner, and a wide transparisteel viewport offers views directly through the cockpit's aft hull. Both TIE/sf seats are equipped with ejection systems.

Although the TIE/sf and TIE/fo share the same overall dimensions and are similar in appearance, the resemblance is largely superficial, and the respective crafts feature numerous unique and non-interchangeable components. Unlike the TIE/fo, which houses a single ion reactor aft of the pilot's seat, the TIE/sf derives power from twin reactors set on either side of the command pod. Because the TIE/sf's additional armament, shield generators, and power-cell banks create more heat than a standard TIE can dissipate, Sienar-Jaemus designers incorporated an experimental ion-flux cooling system to prevent overheating. The combined weight of the TIE/sf's exclusive features make the craft substantially heavier than the TIE/fo.

◀ **First Order Star Destroyers have hangar racks to rotate, deploy, and recover TIE/sf space superiority fighters.**

◀ A heavy weapons turret, limited hyperdrive, and enhanced deflector shield projectors make the Special Forces TIE fighter more robust than the First Order's standard TIE fighter.

▶ Red flashes on the cockpit's port-side and a ventral heavy laser turret visually distinguish the TIE/sf from the standard TIE/fo.

SPECIFICATIONS TIE/sf SPACE SUPERIORITY FIGHTER

MANUFACTURER:
Sienar-Jaemus
Fleet Systems
AFFILIATION: First Order
MODEL: TIE/sf space
superiority fighter
CLASS: Starfighter
LENGTH: 6.7 m (22 ft)
WIDTH: 6.3 m (20 ft 10 in)
HEIGHT: 8.2 m (26 ft 11 in)

MAXIMUM ACCELERATION: 4,450 G
MEGALIGHT PER HOUR: 140
MAXIMUM SPEED (ATMOSPHERE):
1,250kph (777 mph)
ENGINE: SJFS P-s6 twin ion engine
HYPERDRIVE: Class 2
SHIELDING: Equipped
NAVIGATION SYSTEM: Torplex
flight computer

TARGETING SYSTEMS: T-sj1a
targeting computer
ARMAMENT: 2 L-s9.6 laser
cannons (fore); Lb-14 dual heavy
laser turret (aft); missile launcher
ESCAPE CRAFT: Ejector seat
CREW: 2 (1 pilot, 1 gunner)
LIFE SUPPORT: Equipped
CONSUMABLES: 5 days
COST: 190,000 credits

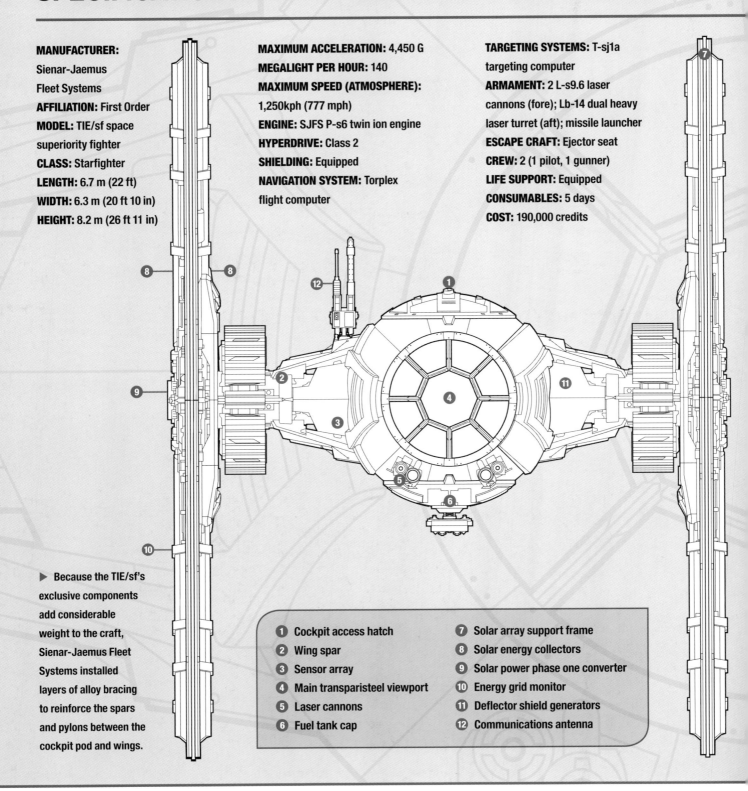

▶ Because the TIE/sf's exclusive components add considerable weight to the craft, Sienar-Jaemus Fleet Systems installed layers of alloy bracing to reinforce the spars and pylons between the cockpit pod and wings.

1 Cockpit access hatch
2 Wing spar
3 Sensor array
4 Main transparisteel viewport
5 Laser cannons
6 Fuel tank cap
7 Solar array support frame
8 Solar energy collectors
9 Solar power phase one converter
10 Energy grid monitor
11 Deflector shield generators
12 Communications antenna

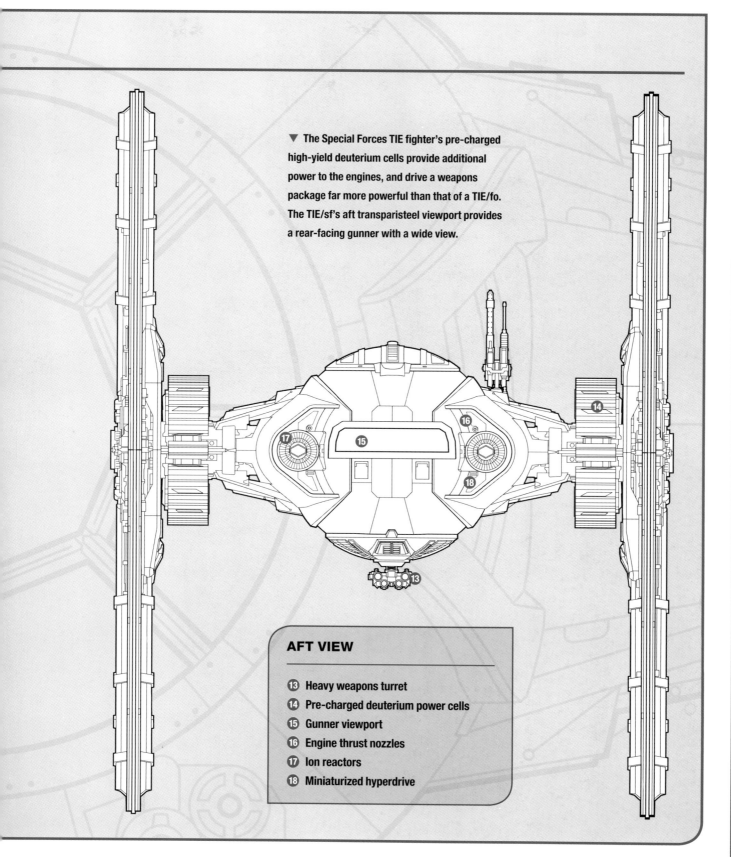

The Special Forces TIE fighter's pre-charged high-yield deuterium cells provide additional power to the engines, and drive a weapons package far more powerful than that of a TIE/fo. The TIE/sf's aft transparisteel viewport provides a rear-facing gunner with a wide view.

AFT VIEW

13 Heavy weapons turret
14 Pre-charged deuterium power cells
15 Gunner viewport
16 Engine thrust nozzles
17 Ion reactors
18 Miniaturized hyperdrive

KYLO REN'S TIE SILENCER

Working in collaboration with engineers at Sienar-Jaemus Fleet Systems, First Order officials revived the Imperial TIE Defender, which First Order tacticians regarded as a versatile attack craft. But the First Order's desire to bring heavier weapons to the battlefield, and also advances in power storage and conversion systems, encouraged the First Order to create an entirely new prototype starfighter. For the prototype, Sienar-Jaemus designers took inspiration from the reinforced aft of the Imperial TIE Advanced x1, the "bent" dagger-shaped wings of the TIE Infiltrator, and the hybrid fighter-bomber aspects of the TIE Defender.

The result was the TIE vendetta space superiority fighter, which designers initially abbreviated as the TIE/vn. Engineers were still working on the prototype when First Order officials dubbed the craft the TIE silencer. The TIE silencer's First Order technological innovations include improved power storage, energy conversion, and experimental stealth gear that blocks sensors and tracking scanners from enemy ships. Utilizing systems from other First Order fighters, designers reconfigured the weapons package of the Special Forces TIE fighter to

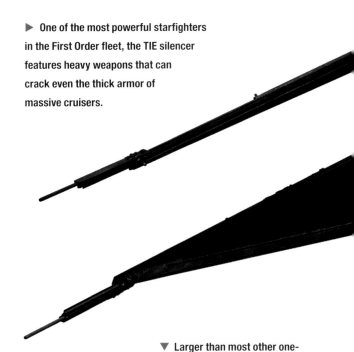

▶ One of the most powerful starfighters in the First Order fleet, the TIE silencer features heavy weapons that can crack even the thick armor of massive cruisers.

▼ Larger than most other one-pilot starfighters, the TIE silencer prototype is both fast and agile.

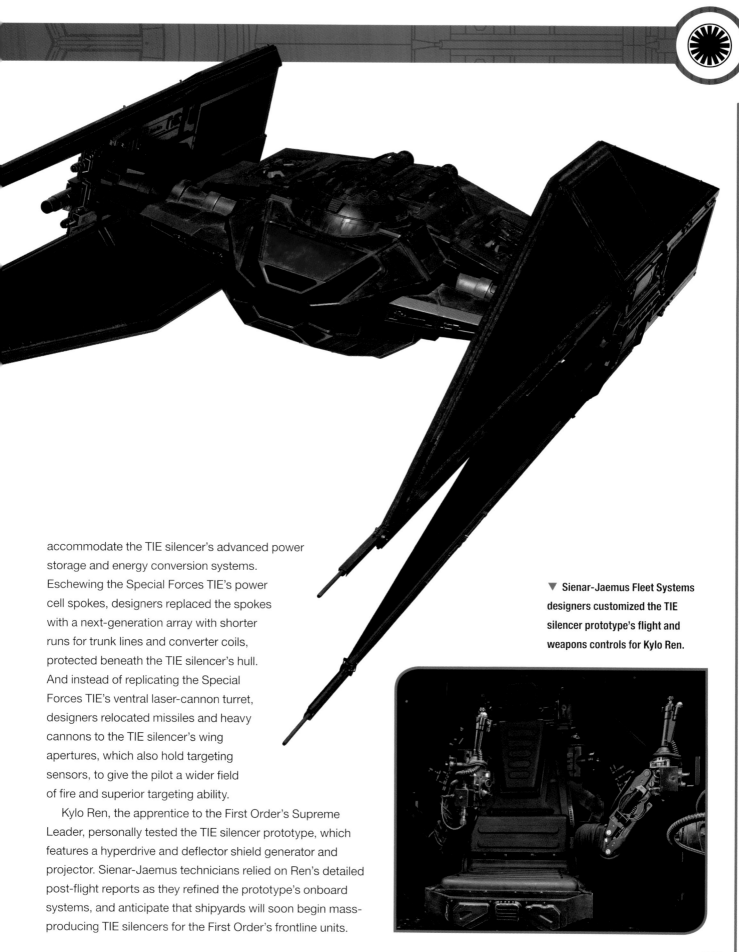

accommodate the TIE silencer's advanced power storage and energy conversion systems. Eschewing the Special Forces TIE's power cell spokes, designers replaced the spokes with a next-generation array with shorter runs for trunk lines and converter coils, protected beneath the TIE silencer's hull. And instead of replicating the Special Forces TIE's ventral laser-cannon turret, designers relocated missiles and heavy cannons to the TIE silencer's wing apertures, which also hold targeting sensors, to give the pilot a wider field of fire and superior targeting ability.

Kylo Ren, the apprentice to the First Order's Supreme Leader, personally tested the TIE silencer prototype, which features a hyperdrive and deflector shield generator and projector. Sienar-Jaemus technicians relied on Ren's detailed post-flight reports as they refined the prototype's onboard systems, and anticipate that shipyards will soon begin mass-producing TIE silencers for the First Order's frontline units.

▼ Sienar-Jaemus Fleet Systems designers customized the TIE silencer prototype's flight and weapons controls for Kylo Ren.

SPECIFICATIONS KYLO REN'S TIE SILENCER

MANUFACTURER: Sienar-Jaemus Fleet Systems

AFFILIATION: First Order

MODEL: TIE/vn prototype

CLASS: Starfighter

LENGTH: 17.4 m (57 ft 2 in)

WIDTH: 7.6 m (25 ft)

HEIGHT: 3.8 m (12 ft 4 in)

MAXIMUM ACCELERATION: 4,500 G

MEGALIGHT PER HOUR: 155

MAXIMUM SPEED (ATMOSPHERE): 1,850 kph (1,150 mph)

ENGINE: Twin ion engine

HYPERDRIVE: Equipped

SHIELDING: Deflector shell generator and projector

NAVIGATION SYSTEM: Torplex flight computer

TARGETING SYSTEMS: Equipped

ARMAMENT: SJFS L-s9.6 medium laser cannons (4); SJFS L-7.5 heavy laser cannons (2); missile launchers (2)

ESCAPE CRAFT: Ejector seat

CREW: Pilot (1)

LIFE SUPPORT: Equipped

CONSUMABLES: 5 days

COST: 310,000 credits

▲ Kylo Ren, like his grandfather Anakin Skywalker, is a naturally skilled pilot.

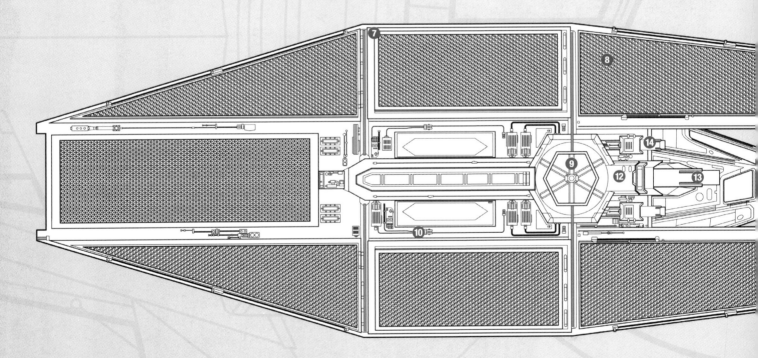

▲ Although the TIE silencer's length is several meters less than that of the Empire's strictly atmospheric TIE/rp reaper attack lander, the TIE silencer is more than six meters longer than the Imperial TIE/d Defender Elite, and has the distinction of being the longest model TIE starfighter to date.

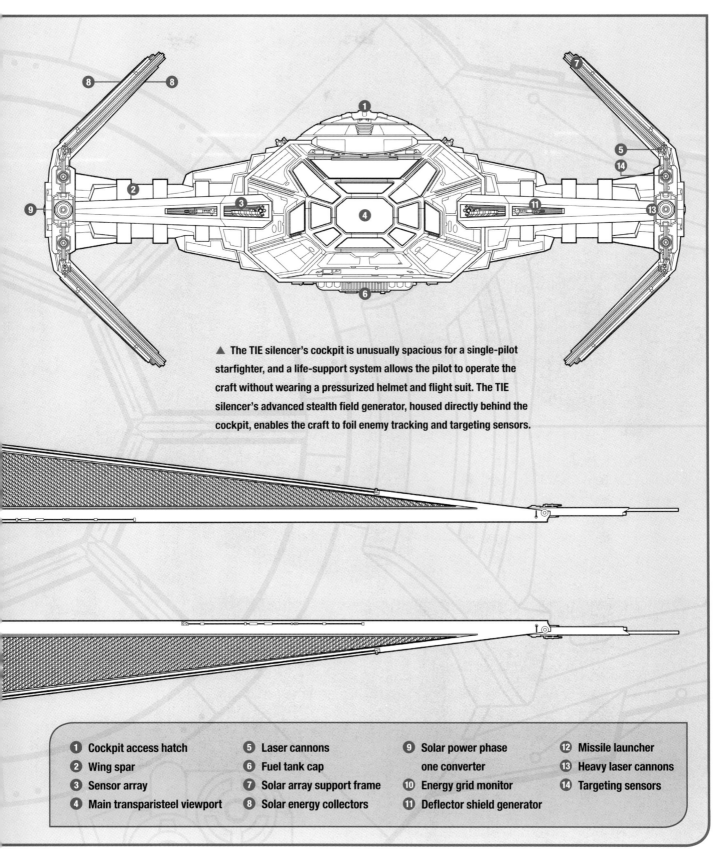

▲ The TIE silencer's cockpit is unusually spacious for a single-pilot starfighter, and a life-support system allows the pilot to operate the craft without wearing a pressurized helmet and flight suit. The TIE silencer's advanced stealth field generator, housed directly behind the cockpit, enables the craft to foil enemy tracking and targeting sensors.

1. Cockpit access hatch
2. Wing spar
3. Sensor array
4. Main transparisteel viewport
5. Laser cannons
6. Fuel tank cap
7. Solar array support frame
8. Solar energy collectors
9. Solar power phase one converter
10. Energy grid monitor
11. Deflector shield generator
12. Missile launcher
13. Heavy laser cannons
14. Targeting sensors

WEAPONS & DEFENSIVE SYSTEMS

"Today, after years of training, we embark on our first official mission for the First Order. Because I've worked with each and every one of you, and did my best to transform you from a gang of grunts into a team of pilots, I know you're all eager to climb into your TIE fighters so we can fly off and make history. But before that happens, you'll have to stand at attention for another minute so I can tell you about the most important weapons at your disposal. And what I'm going to tell you is off the books, something that I doubt very much you've ever heard before.

We follow in the tradition of Imperial TIE fighter pilots, whose primary weapons were a pair of Sienar Fleet Systems L-s1 laser cannons. Because some of you began your training using our older flight simulators, you know the Imperial TIE fighter cannons were state-of-the-art, but now, we might best describe them as serviceable. I don't say that with any disrespect to Imperial pilots, who fired those cannons as they flew bravely in starfighters that lacked even basic deflector shields. I merely want to emphasize that we have the advantage of technological advances in weapons, advances that our forebears could only dream of.

The First Order has provided us with Sienar-Jaemus Fleet Systems L-s9.6 laser cannons. I'm confident that you all know how to operate these cannons, upside down and with your eyes closed. The reason I'm confident is because it's my duty to make sure you can handle your laser cannons under any and all circumstances. So don't expect any last-minute pep talks or instructions from me about laser cannons. Because the fact is that your laser cannons are not the most important weapons at your disposal.

So which weapons are the most important? I'll make it easy for you. Take a good look at each other. Now, take a good look at yourselves.

When you climb into your cockpit, and settle into your seat, and ease your finger close to the trigger on your control stick, know that the TIE fighter and its cannons are nothing without the instrument that makes them operational. You are that instrument. *You* are the weapon. Let's fly."

— Jad "Scorch" Bean, First Order TIE fighter flight instructor and Commander of Zeta Squadron

◀ A First Order pilot adjusts the weapons and targeting controls inside the cockpit of a TIE/fo fighter.

LASER CANNONS

Sienar Fleet Systems armed Imperial TIE fighters with two SFS L-s1 laser cannons, which were mounted inside the craft's spherical hull. The military-grade cannons fired bolts of concentrated energy, projectiles that were capable of destroying enemy starfighters with a single shot.

Operating under the same principles as blaster weaponry, laser cannons convert energy-rich gas to a glowing particle beam that can pierce, melt through, and even disintegrate targets. Different gases produce different colored lasers, with red being the most common, as the gas that yields red particle beams was and remains the least expensive. For the Imperial TIE fighter, Sienar used a more expensive gas that yielded green particle beams, which enabled TIE pilots to track their own laserfire during combat, and more

▲ Two SFS L-s7.2 laser cannons embedded in the cockpit module's hull became the TIE/in's standard weapons.

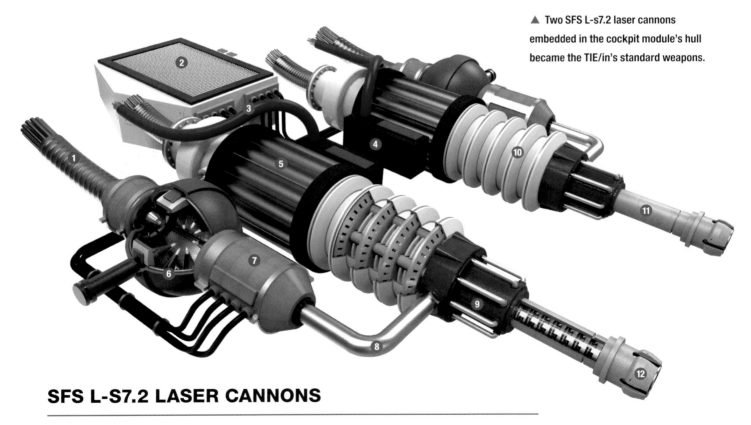

SFS L-S7.2 LASER CANNONS

1 Primary reactor power lines

2 Fire control computer

3 Gas supply line

4 Gas injector control relay

5 Preliminary impulse chamber

6 Laser reactor chamber

7 Laser power converter

8 Crystal power conduit

9 Prismatic crystal housing

10 XCiter

11 Galvenning barrel

12 Final stage collimator

▶ The TIE/fo fighter's high-pressure radioactive gas fuel tank provides energy for craft's SJFS L-s9.6 laser cannons.

easily distinguish their allies from their foes during dogfights. Imperial TIE fighter cannons were capable of rapid fire but were prone to overheating.

In early TIE fighter models, the lasers drew power from the craft's ion engines, but this reduced maneuverability during heavy combat, when pilots used the lasers frequently. Sienar retrofitted the early models to accommodate a separate power generator, which increased the lasers' range and lethality. The separate power generator became a standard in all subsequently manufactured Imperial TIE fighters.

The Imperial Navy eventually replaced the SFS L-s1 laser cannons with SFS L-s7.2 laser cannons, an improved design that offered a low recycle time and higher rates of fire. By the time of the Battle of Endor, the Navy considered the SFS L-s7.2 laser cannons as the standard weapons for TIE fighters.

FIRST ORDER LASER CANNONS

Sienar-Jaemus Fleet Systems designed and manufactured the L-s9.6 laser cannon for the TIE/fo space superiority fighter. Each fighter holds two L-s9.6 cannons, which are positioned below each side of the command cockpit module. On First Order TIE fighter flight controls, the right-control column houses the weapons trigger. In keeping with the tradition of Imperial TIE fighters, First Order TIE fighter laser cannons release green laserfire.

▶ Illuminated in red, targeting sensor optics increase accuracy for the TIE/fo's SJFS L-s9.6 laser cannons.

PROTON TORPEDO LAUNCHER, TORPEDOES, & BOMBS

The Imperial TIE/sa bomber carried launchers for a variety of explosive munitions. Sienar Fleet Systems designed and manufactured the bomber's primary missile-firing weapons, a pair of SFS T-s5 torpedo launchers. Each T-s5 held a standard load of four torpedoes but Imperial technicians could modify the launchers to hold six torpedoes. Merr-Sonn Munitions manufactured and supplied the Imperial Navy with LX-4 proton torpedoes, explosive warheads that Merr-Sonn simultaneously retrofitted and marketed as LX-4 proton mines.

TIE bombers typically fired proton torpedoes at long-range targets. Upon impact, the torpedoes released clouds of high-velocity proton particles. Upgraded torpedoes possessed target-locking capability that was exceptionally maneuverable, and able to make a 90-degree turn within a turning circle of one meter.

Sienar also equipped the Imperial TIE bomber with two SFS M-s3 concussion missile launchers. Each M-s3 held a standard load of eight missiles but could be modified to hold ten missiles. Each concussion missile was a short-range missile that featured an armor-piercing tip, and which released clouds of high-velocity proton particles upon impact. The concussion blast not only damaged the area of impact but also disrupted surrounding instruments and equipment.

The Imperial TIE bomber's bomb bay held a variable load of ordnance. Payloads included ArmaTek SJ-62/68 orbital mines, ArmaTek VL-61/79 proton bombs, and Merr-Sonn Munitions thermal detonators, which were powered by volatile barium and had a blast radius of 20 meters. Unlike thermal detonators with manual triggers, the TIE bomber released detonators that could be activated by electronic transmission from the bomber pilot.

ARMATEK VL-61/79 PROTON BOMB

1. Implosion detonator
2. Lanthanide alloy outer skin
3. Implosion dampers
4. Neuranium reaction-containment shield
5. Proton-generating reactor core

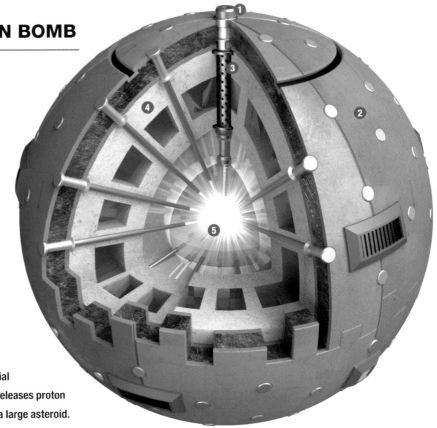

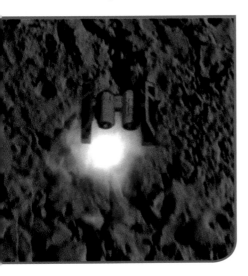

◀ An Imperial TIE bomber releases proton bombs over a large asteroid.

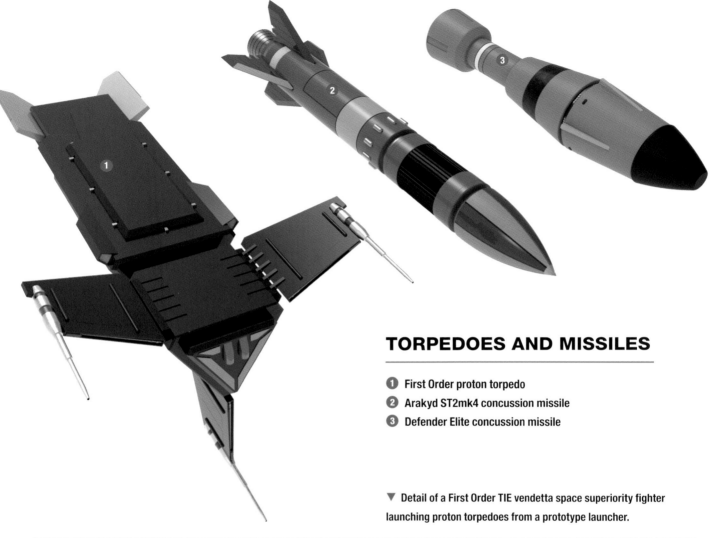

TORPEDOES AND MISSILES

1 First Order proton torpedo
2 Arakyd ST2mk4 concussion missile
3 Defender Elite concussion missile

▼ Detail of a First Order TIE vendetta space superiority fighter launching proton torpedoes from a prototype launcher.

EJECTOR SEAT

Sienar Fleet Systems equipped all Imperial TIE fighters with ejector seats. Imperial academies trained pilots to only eject from their fighters after they had exhausted all other options, but because TIE pilots wore pressurized flight suits and helmets, they were always ready to eject directly into space if such action were absolutely necessary.

During startup procedures, the TIE pilot pulled a lever to arm the ejection system. In emergencies, the pilot pulled a lower lever that simultaneously blasted open the cockpit access hatch, and ignited the explosive launcher mechanism built into the base of the seat. The seat rose up guide rails, and the parachute was automatically primed for deployment in atmospheres as the seat launched through the hatch.

If the seat ejected in atmospheres with gravitational forces, the seat's sensors, antigrav unit, and automated safety systems would adjust to prevent spinal fractures. If the seat ejected in space, the same safety systems would attempt to guide the pilot away from shattered fragments of the pilot's own TIE fighter, nearby asteroids, and other hazardous debris. The seat's sensors would determine whether to release the pilot from the seat or keep the pilot restrained to the seat. In atmospheres, the safety systems released the pilot from the seat before deploying a parachute from the pilot's backpack.

The seat's built-in personnel locator beacon transmitted a signal to nearby Imperial vessels, enabling rescue crews to recover the pilot. For recovery operations in space, Imperial crews typically used tractor beams to draw the ejected pilot into a rescue craft.

All First Order TIE fighters are similarly equipped with ejector seats.

◄ Utilizing the same aerospace technologies as Imperial TIE fighter ejector seats, First Order TIE fighter ejector seats use a combination of antigrav technology and automatic parachutes to help pilots descend slowly.

❶ Top hatch impact guard
❷ Headrest
❸ Seat restraints
❹ Height adjustment actuator
❺ Backpad
❻ Parachute housing
❼ Emergency restraint release
❽ Ejector seat arming lever
❾ Ejector seat release
❿ Harness buckle
⓫ Personnel locator beacon
⓬ Survival kit
⓭ Leg restraint actuators
⓮ Launch guide rails
⓯ Explosive launcher mechanism
⓰ Antigrav unit

FLIGHT DATA RECORDER

Nearly every spacefaring ship in the galaxy carries a flight data recorder. The device contains complete records of a craft's range, top speed, shield array, weapons payload, performance parameters, and recent travel history.

For Imperial TIE fighters, Sienar Fleet Systems engineered and constructed a box-shaped flight data recorder to withstand the force of a high-speed impact, intense heat and cold, and hazardous radiation. An armored compartment, located below the TIE fighter pilot's seat, housed the durable recorder. Sienar equipped the recorder with a transponder that allowed Imperial authorities to locate and recover the device in the event that it became separated from the rest of the fighter.

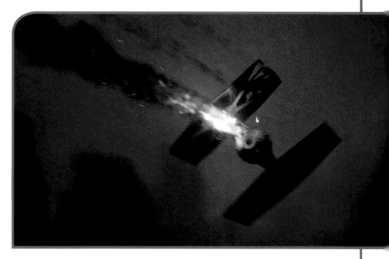

▲ Enemy laserfire and high-speed impacts may reduce a TIE fighter to shredded, unidentifiable debris, but Sienar Fleet Systems guarantees the craft's heavily protected flight data recorder will remain intact.

1 Insulated memory cores
2 Cockpit microphone
3 Reinforced housing
4 Locator beacon
5 Power status indicator
6 Flight system interface
7 Vehicle power connect

TIE PILOTS, TRAINING, AND GEAR

"Listen carefully, cadets. I've reviewed your dossiers, psychological profiles, and everything that the Imperial Security Bureau has on you. I am confident that I now know more about each of you than you ever wanted anyone to know.

Some of you hail from worlds that were steeped in military traditions long before the Clone Wars made the most pacifistic senators of the old Republic acknowledge that your heritage had value. Some of you come from backwater worlds where you learned to operate aircraft and spacecraft for pleasure, while others learned as a matter of survival. Some of you grew up with great wealth. Others have criminal records dating back to childhood. I know your accomplishments and ambitions, your failures and regrets, and quite probably every secret that you thought you'd take to your grave.

But your life before this moment is done. Over. Finished. The only thing that matters is why you are here, right now, at Skystrike Academy.

You are here because the Empire sees the potential in you to join the ranks of its most elite pilots. Most of you will fail. Whatever you have achieved before means nothing. Here, only the best survive.

Given that the odds are already against you... Why, then, did I bother studying your records in such exhaustive detail? Because my duty as a flight instructor is to train you to the best of my ability, which means I'll be pushing you beyond your own abilities, and doing everything I can to bring you up to Imperial standards. That's another way of saying I aim to bring you up to my standards. And in my effort to transform you into the most deadly instruments of the Imperial Navy, I needed to know about you the same way that a mechanic needs to know every tool at his disposal.

And be advised that I am a very skilled mechanic. I already know which tools work better than others. I also know which tools have their limitations, and which can be repurposed. I know which tools have singular functions, and which ones are useful for various tasks.

And I know the most important thing of all, the one thing you must know to be true if you are ever to become an Imperial TIE fighter pilot. Like any tool, you are expendable and replaceable.

During training assignments and missions, you will address each other by comm numbers only. Prepare yourselves. Your first combat training will begin at 0600. Squadron dismissed."

—Imperial TIE Fighter Flight Instructor Goran at the Skystrike Academy, Montross

TRAINING ACADEMIES

IMPERIAL ACADEMIES

Prior to the Clone Wars, numerous academies in Republic space offered training for starpilots, but the only organized military schools were affiliated with regional planetary security forces that served to defend their homeworlds against pirates and invaders. But when Separatists and renegade trade unions threatened to wreak havoc throughout Republic space, Chancellor Palpatine quickly formed the Grand Army of the Republic to restore peace. The Grand Army consisted almost entirely of cloned soldiers who received their training at the cloning factories on Kamino, and who took their orders from Jedi Generals, but also included enlisted officers from the aforementioned security forces. When the Clone Wars ended and the Republic transitioned into the Galactic Empire, the Imperial Army and Navy absorbed existing military academies and also founded new academies to train cadets to become pilots, officers, and infantry soldiers for the Empire's newly formed regiments.

Worlds with notable Imperial Academies included Coruscant, Montross, Raithal, Arkanis, Carida, and Corulag.

The Royal Imperial Academy on Coruscant was one of the premier academies. The Royal Academy had a three-year program that required cadets to study science, mathematics, and piloting, and provided comprehensive courses in hand-to-hand combat, sharpshooting, and battle strategies. Because the Royal Academy promoted intense competition, severe rules, and near constant testing, only ten percent of cadets graduated from the Imperial pilot training program.

The same washout rate applied to cadets enrolled at the Skystrike Academy, an elite starfighter academy at Montross. Under the administration of Instructor Goran and Captain Vult Skerris, the Skystrike Academy produced some of the best TIE fighter pilots in the Imperial Navy. The Skystrike Academy also trained pilots to fly TIE bombers, Imperial landing craft, and other vessels.

◄ A career military man, Wilhuff Tarkin served the Outland Regions Security Force's anti-pirate task force, and attended Sullust Sector Spacefarers Academy before he became an Admiral in the Grand Republic Navy. Emperor Palpatine appointed Tarkin as the first Grand Moff of the Imperial Navy.

▶ Imperial Armed Forces recruitment centers, such as the one at Coronet Spaceport on Corellia, promoted military career opportunities for citizens of the galaxy.

FIRST ORDER ACADEMIES

Following the destruction of the second Death Star and the signing of the Galactic Concordance, a group of Imperial loyalists relocated to the Unknown Regions and established their own military academies to serve what would become the First Order. At First Order academies, TIE fighter pilots undergo rigorous training not unlike the constant drilling of their stormtrooper cadet counterparts. Pilots begin training in childhood, and most mature within the corridors of Star Destroyers. The First Order maintains strict standards of reflexes, visual acuity, and hand-eye coordination. TIE fighter pilots who fail to meet First Order standards are transferred to other assignments within the fleet.

▶ The son of an Imperial instructor at the Arkanis Academy, Armitage Hux rose through the ranks of the First Order to become a General of the High Command.

SIMULATOR PODS

Sienar Fleet Systems manufactured TIE fighter flight-simulator pods for the purpose of training cadets at Imperial Academies and the Imperial Navy. Resembling standalone cockpit pods from standard TIE/in fighters, the simulator pods hovered between a pair of brackets equipped with maneuverable tractor beam projectors that were linked to the cockpit controls. A pilot operating the controls could rotate the pod 360 degrees in any direction to simulate the experience of flying a TIE fighter. Academy training facilities typically housed 12 simulator pods in a single chamber to instruct 12 cadets simultaneously so that the cadets would learn to operate together as a squadron.

Before boarding simulator pods, cadets donned pressurized flight suits and helmets. Each cadet ascended steps on an access stand to arrive above a pod's hatch and climb down into the cockpit. The pod's interior and controls were identical to an actual TIE fighter with one exception: instead of traditional transparisteel viewports, the pod's viewports displayed interactive holograms of space and planetary environments, spacecraft and asteroids. Thus, a cadet looking "through" the pod's viewport saw extremely realistic environments, and also saw the TIE fighters operated by fellow cadets and wingmen as they "flew" together on training missions and combat exercises.

Sienar equipped simulator pods with exotic audio, vibration, and gravity technology that reproduced the flight characteristics of TIE fighters with incredible accuracy, and which delivered realistic cues to the cadets in real time. If cadets "pursued" targets through simulated atmospheric environments, their bodies would shift in their seats as if they were experiencing actual gravitational forces, or jounce when they experienced "turbulence". And if a simulated enemy starfighter's laserfire "struck" a cadet's pod, the cadet would feel the impact.

Academy flight instructors monitored training exercises on computer viewscreens that could display simulated exterior images of cadets' "'TIE fighters" in real time, and from any perspective, enabling instructors to examine exercises from different vantage points. Instructors could also watch exercises from the cadets' respective points of view.

After cadets graduated from the academies and joined the Imperial Navy, they continued to train and hone their skills on simulator pods. To ensure that TIE fighter pilots never lost their edge, simulator pods were a standard feature on most Imperial warships, including Star Destroyers.

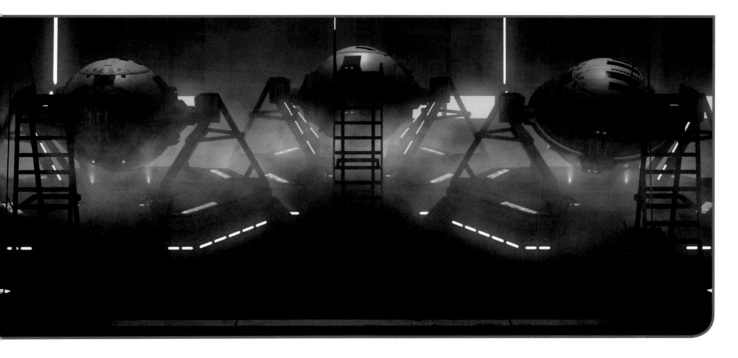

1. Cockpit access hatch
2. Image generator
3. Pitch axis servos
4. Yaw axis track
5. Roll axis servos
6. Processor housing
7. Instructor controls
8. Ladder docking slot

◀ Skystrike Academy cadets honed their piloting skills in Imperial TIE fighter simulator pods.

▶ Cadets climb mobile access stands to enter and exit simulator pods.

COMBAT TACTICS

Although numerous technological advances make First Order TIE fighters superior to Imperial TIE fighters, starfighter combat tactics remain largely unchanged. Adhering to Imperial Navy dictates, First Order academy tacticians maintain that starfighter combat can be broken up into five stages: detection, closing, attack, maneuver, and disengagement.

In detection, pilots detect possible threats visually or by the starfighter's sensors. After detecting a possible threat, the pilot must positively identify the object, spacecraft, or vessel, and also evaluate the threat. TIE fighters have sensors linked to a data-sorting computer, enabling pilots to easily detect other spacecraft and identify opponents. Because some enemies use sensor-jamming technology or camouflage, First Order academies train pilots to rely equally on their eyes as well as their sensors.

If the pilot chooses to engage the threat, the pilot will attempt to attain an advantageous position for an attack run, the combat tactic known as closing. The two essential elements of closing are speed and concealment, as both aid in limiting the amount of time the opponent has to react to the attack.

The single most decisive stage of starfighter combat is the attack stage, which accounts for four out of every five starfighter kills. A head-on attack will almost always result in a quick victory for one pilot or the other. First Order combat pilot instructors profess that the best avenue for attack is to approach the enemy from astern, and refer to this vulnerable target area as the "prime target cone". The closer a TIE pilot angles into the intended target's stern, the more likely the pilot can fire a devastating shot.

The maneuver stage of combat occurs only when a pilot's initial attack fails, and the intended target returns fire and pursues the pilot. This situation can result in a dogfight. In maneuvering out of an attack, a pilot's first priority is to

HEAD-ON COUNTERVAIL

▲ When an enemy starfighter approaches for a head-on attack, the TIE pilot can swerve hard and fast before turning after the enemy. The superior turning ability of TIE fighters prompted Imperial TIE fighter pilots to popularize this maneuver.

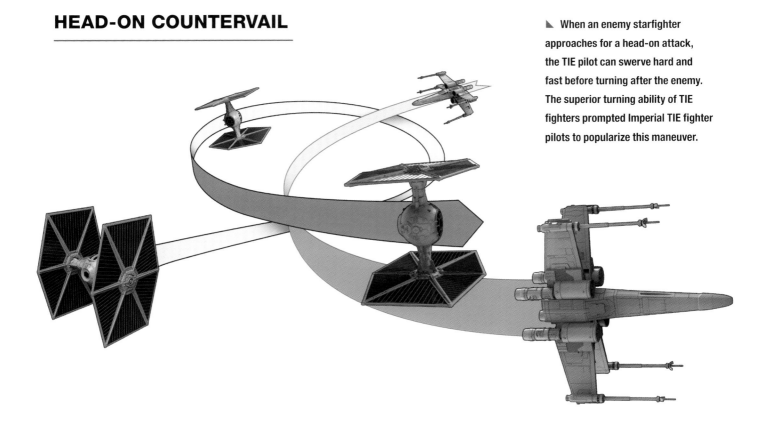

REVERSE THROTTLE HOP

1. Attacker approaches at high closure speed
2. Defender performs evasive turn
3. Attacker ascends vertically, executes a full roll
4. Attacker pulls through, keeping defender in sight
5. Attacker closes, fires at target

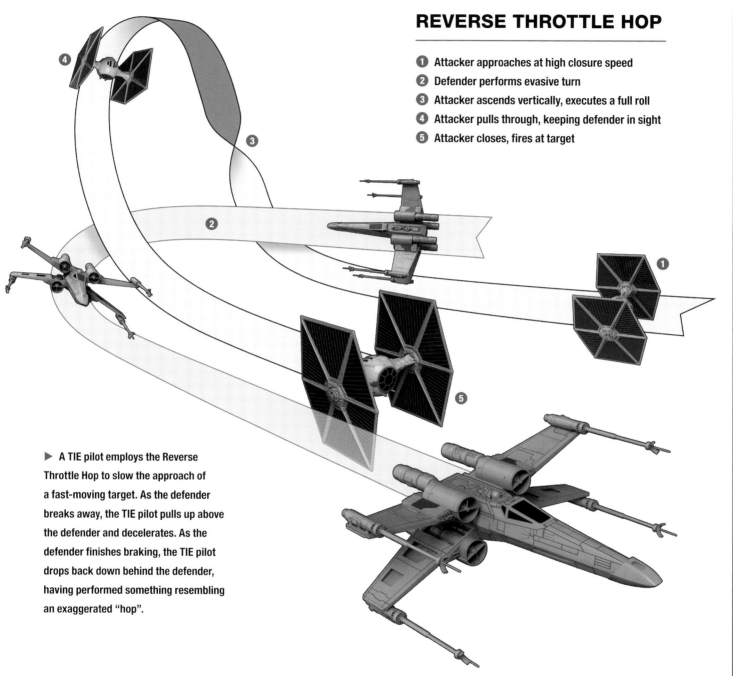

▶ A TIE pilot employs the Reverse Throttle Hop to slow the approach of a fast-moving target. As the defender breaks away, the TIE pilot pulls up above the defender and decelerates. As the defender finishes braking, the TIE pilot drops back down behind the defender, having performed something resembling an exaggerated "hop".

survive, and the second priority is to turn the tables on the enemy, ideally by attacking the target's stern. The first pilot who makes a mistake is almost always the loser.

Combat pilot instructors emphasize that the importance of the final stage of combat, disengagement, cannot be overstated. After a successful attack pass, even experienced pilots may feel a momentary sense of accomplishment that prompts them to let down their guard, and forget that they

could remain vulnerable to attack by incoming fighters. Unless TIE fighter pilots completely destroy all enemy fighters in a designated area, and unless commanding officers order pilots to remain in that area, the most effective method of disengagement is to angle off at full-throttle and escape into hyperspace. If possible, TIE fighter pilots should consider a plan for disengagement before closing for an attack.

TIE HANGAR RACKS

When the Imperial Navy commissioned Sienar Fleet Systems to manufacture a line of inexpensive short-range starfighters that would, by design, not only discourage Imperial pilots from deserting but inhibit their ability to stray from the fleet, Navy officials were not surprised to learn that Sienar's TIE fighter was without a hyperdrive, deflector shields, or built-in life-support systems. However, the Imperial Records Office revealed that several Navy officials were initially confounded by the fact that the TIE fighter also lacked one particular piece of equipment that was standard on nearly all starfighters: landing gear. As the officials prepared to question Raith Sienar's designs for the TIE fighter, Sienar himself presented the schematics for a system of cycling racks to store and release the fighters within hangars.

A masterpiece of engineering, Imperial SFS TIE cycling racks held up to 72 starfighters in larger hangars. Pilots boarded their TIE fighters from overhead gantries, and the rack's automated systems advanced each fighter toward the front position, where the launch rack disengaged the fighters and released them either within the hangar or directly into space. When the launch rack released TIE fighters within the hangar, tractor beam controllers would guide the fighters through the hangar's magnetic forcefield and into space.

Tractor beam controllers guided returning TIE fighters into separate hangars, and to waiting receiver-carriers. The receivers carried the TIE fighters to a debarkation station where the pilots exited. Afterward, TIE fighters passed through a separate bay for refueling and any necessary maintenance by astromech droids before automated systems sent the fighters through transfer tunnels to a launch hangar. In the launch hangar, the TIE fighters cycled back into the launch rack, ready for their next mission.

Raith Sienar noted that the TIE fighters' lack of landing gear reduced mass for maximum maneuverability, and also that the fighters were structurally capable of resting on their wings. Navy officials admired the economy of Sienar's designs, and further appreciated how the TIE fighter and its related racking system served to teach Imperial pilots to rely completely on higher authority.

▲ The Shield Gate, a wheel-shaped Imperial space station and planetary deflector shield generator in orbit of the Outer Rim world Scarif, housed racks that unleashed swarms of TIE fighters to counter a Rebel attack.

◄ The First Order adopted and upgraded cycling racks for TIE fighters in their own warships, including hangars within the *Finalizer*, a *Resurgent*-class Star Destroyer.

HANGAR RACKS

1. Ship gantry
2. Pilot catwalk
3. Boarding platform
4. Ladder
5. Cockpit access hatch
6. Main transparisteel viewport
7. Retaining claw
8. Launch release guide

▶ Sienar Fleet Systems engineered adjustable, modular rack launching systems for Imperial TIE fighters. Imperial technicians could expand and reconfigure the racks to fit the maximum number of TIE fighters into hangars of virtually any size.

MAINTENANCE AND TECHNICAL SUPPORT

Although the Empire relied on many automated systems to coordinate and perform the maintenance, deployment, and recovery of Imperial TIE fighters, the Empire also utilized skilled technicians and ground crews to assist with TIE fighter operations aboard warships as well as at spaceports and ground-based installations. At Imperial surface ports, dedicated personnel helped direct traffic on busy landing fields with rapidly changing traffic, where automated systems could not typically make decisions fast enough.

Imperial deck technicians wore sensor-laden helmets with built-in headsets that linked them to air traffic controllers, and wielded illuminated traffic wands to signal to pilots and guide them to designated landing areas. Deck technicians also wore piloting gear, as they were authorized to commandeer certain vessels across landing decks. Despite the versatile and easily accessible technological tools within their helmets, most deck technicians became accustomed to eyeballing distances without sensors, and used other analog solutions to accomplish their duties.

▼ **A deck technician carries out instructions from air traffic control.**

▶ **An Imperial deck technician waves traffic wands to guide a TIE fighter to a landing pad.**

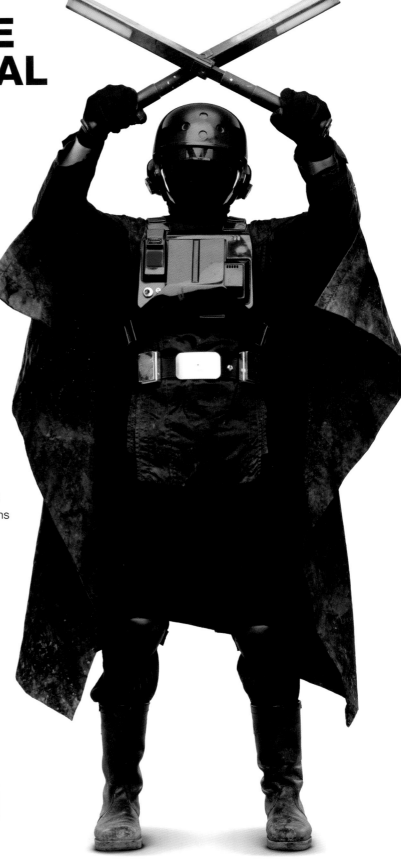

▶ Deck technicians make sure TIE fighters are fully operational before leaving hangars.

IMPERIAL ASTROMECH DROIDS

By the direction of the Imperial Navy, Sienar Fleet Systems constructed Imperial TIE fighters without any accommodation for onboard astromech droids to perform navigational duties and emergency repairs. However, Industrial Automaton R-series astromechs served as standard equipment in Imperial hangars, docking bays, and military installations, where the droids carried out routine maintenance, repairs, and technological diagnostics on vehicles and vessels.

Industrial Automaton manufactured durable and reprogrammable R-series astromechs to service Imperial TIE fighters. Industrial Automaton also manufactured R4 units, which Imperial Press Corps repurposed to serve as couriers to transport data from place to place in lieu of electronic communication networks. Technicians programmed the Imperial astromechs with extremely limited identity parameters, restricting the droids' abilities for independent action to ensure they would focus only on their assigned tasks. The technicians routinely wiped astromech droids' memory banks to prevent the droids from developing distinct and potentially disobedient personalities.

IMPERIAL NAVY
TIE PILOT FLIGHT SUIT

The pilots who flew Imperial capital ships and starfighters formed the mainstay of the Imperial Navy, but all agreed that TIE fighter pilots formed the most elite corps. Most pilot candidates were either graduates of an Imperial Academy or volunteers who came from active Imperial units, and were already certified pilots or astrogators. Each candidate underwent a rigorous screening process, and only ten percent of all candidates passed. Those who did pass were subjected to prolonged and thorough training, including hundreds of hours of actual flight time. The Navy routinely conducted such training from active Star Destroyers in order to expose trainees to the flight environment and the requirements of actual missions.

Psychological conditioning made TIE fighter pilots entirely dedicated to target destruction. Whether assigned to garrison, planetary defense, or fleet duty, nearly all TIE pilots operated in teams. TIE pilots learned to employ tactics that required coordinated efforts, and understood that their combined skill and teamwork was their best chance to survive on missions in their unshielded TIE fighters. Because TIE fighters did not contain life-support systems, pilots relied on their flight suit's life-support systems to stay alive in space.

IMPERIAL NAVY FLIGHT SUIT

1. Reinforced vac-seal flight helmet
2. Ship-linked communications
3. Polarized lenses
4. Vocoder
5. Breathing filters
6. Gas transfer hoses
7. Control switches
8. Reset controls
9. Emergency atmospheric unit
10. Insulated pressure suit
11. Wrist seals
12. Insulated gauntlets
13. Positive-gravity pressure boots

FIRST ORDER
TIE PILOT
FLIGHT SUIT

Whereas the Imperial Navy sent their TIE fighter pilots into combat in unshielded starfighters, and essentially treated them as expendable, the First Order makes deflector shield generators and pressurized cockpits a standard feature on all TIE fighters, and regards their fighter pilots as important parts of their war machine. First Order TIE pilots have no need to worry about the possibility of a micrometeoroid puncturing their fighters and tearing through their flight suits and bodies. On long reconnaissance missions, they can remove their helmets and breathe freely.

Like their First Order stormtrooper counterparts, TIE pilots wear helmets with sophisticated built-in technology: targeting nodes connect to external targeting sensors, and targeting interface projectors enable pilots to more clearly and readily find and fire at their targets.

To find potential TIE pilots, First Order recruiters begin by seeking out children with keen eyes, quick reflexes, and a healthy respect for authority. Not unlike their Imperial predecessors, the best prospects in the First Order Pilot Corps undergo physical training and constant drilling. Because most grow up within the corridors of Star Destroyers, Pilot Corps cadets become intimately familiar with starship operations before they become fully fledged pilots.

FIRST ORDER FLIGHT SUIT

1. Reinforced vac-seal flight helmet
2. Ship-linked communications
3. Polarized lenses
4. Vocoder
5. Breathing filters
6. Gas transfer hose
7. Control switches
8. Reset controls
9. Emergency atmospheric unit
10. Insulated pressure suit
11. Wrist seals
12. Insulated gauntlets and vambrace armor
13. Positive-gravity pressure boots

SIZE COMPARISON CHART

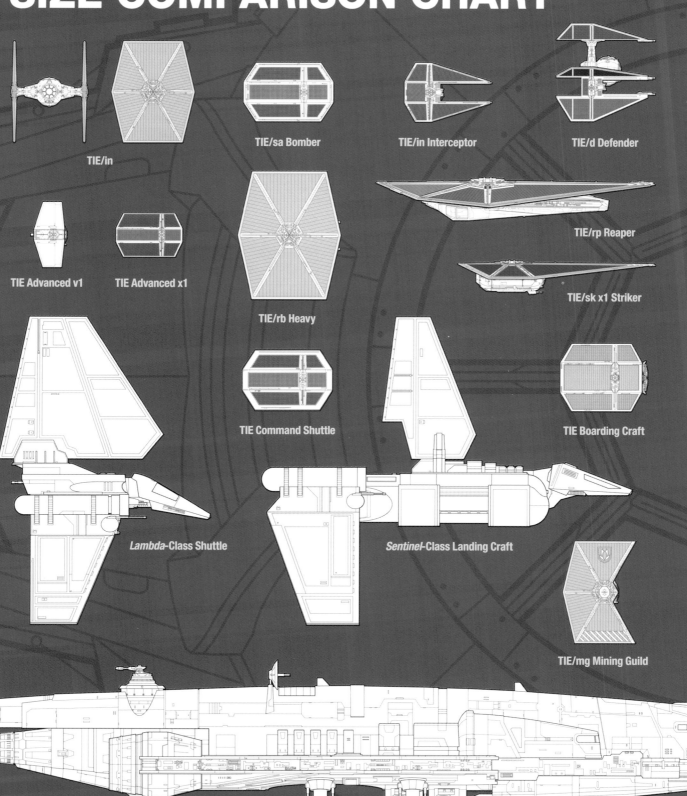

TIE/in

TIE/sa Bomber

TIE/in Interceptor

TIE/d Defender

TIE Advanced v1

TIE Advanced x1

TIE/rb Heavy

TIE/rp Reaper

TIE/sk x1 Striker

TIE Command Shuttle

TIE Boarding Craft

Lambda-Class Shuttle

Sentinel-Class Landing Craft

TIE/mg Mining Guild

Gonzati-Class Cruiser

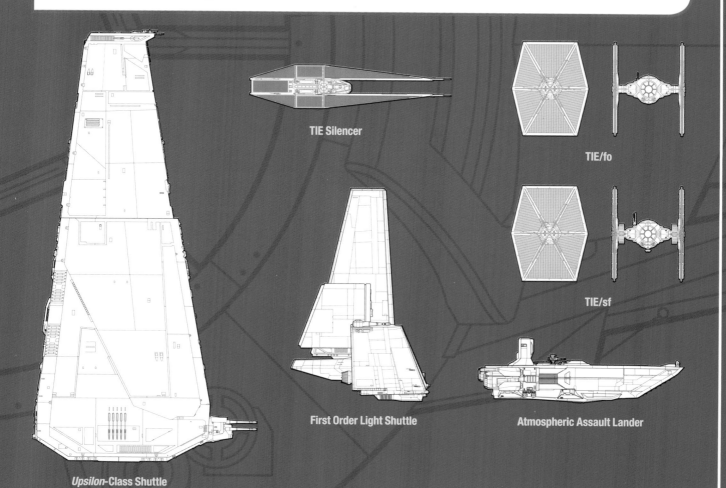

First Order *Resurgent*-Class Star Destroyer

Imperial I-Class Star Destroyer

Imperial I-Class Star Destroyer
(Main hangar detail)

CR90 Corvette

Gonzati-Class Cruiser

Lambda-Class Shuttle

TIE/in Starfighter

TIE Silencer

TIE/fo

TIE/sf

Upsilon-Class Shuttle

First Order Light Shuttle

Atmospheric Assault Lander

ACKNOWLEDGMENTS

The author and artists of the *TIE Fighter Owners' Workshop Manual* utilized information about TIE fighters from many previously published *Star Wars* books, and are indebted to the following writers and artists: Richard Chasemore, Stephen Crane, Jason Fry, Barbara L. Gibson, Greg Gordon, Hans Jenssen, Michael Kogge, Paul Murphy, Timothy S. O'Brien, Kemp Remillard, David West Reynolds, Peter Schweighofer, Bill Slavicsek, Bill Smith, and Curtis Smith. We also gratefully acknowledge George Lucas, John Barry, Colin Cantwell, Joe Johnston, Ralph McQuarrie, Lorne Peterson, Paul Huston, and Norman Reynolds and their colleagues for their significant contributions to TIE fighters in the *Star Wars* movies.

Special thanks to the following people for their help with reference for this project: Jason Eaton for his models of the TIE fighter prototype, the TIE Command Shuttle, and TIE Advanced x1; James Clyne, Vincent Jenkins, and Aaron McBride for their concept art of TIE fighters from *Solo: A Star Wars Story*; Andre Kirk for his concept art for the TIE simulator pod; Jay Machado, modeler at Industrial Light & Magic, for information regarding the TIE boarding craft; Doug Chiang and the Rag Tag team for visualizing the TIE reaper interior; and our friends at Lucasfilm: Leland Chee, Pablo Hidalgo, Samantha Holland, Nicole LaCoursiere, Matt Martin, Bryce Pinkos, Michael Siglain, and Robert Simpson.

▼ Concept art for *The Force Awakens* by Doug Chiang.